WAZEM & PEETERS

KOMA

Pierre Wazem
Writer

Frederik Peeters
Artist

Albertine Ralenti
Colorist

Samantha Demers
for *World Language Communications*
Translator

Alex Donoghue
U.S. Edition Editor

Jerry Frissen
Book Designer

KOMA was first published as a series in six volumes by Les Humanoïdes Associés SAS, Paris.

This omnibus edition published under licence in the EU by Usharp Comics, an imprint of Highland Books Limited, 2 High Pines, Knoll Road, Godalming, GU7 2EP, UK.

ISBN-10: 1-905496-08-7
ISBN-13: 978 1905496 08 2

Printed in China.

CLUNK!

?!?

CLUNK
CLUNK
CLUNK

SSSS

DID YOU
FAINT?

?

YOU FELL! *BAM!* JUST DROPPED! OUT OF NOWHERE!

ORNITHORHYNCHUS!

?

"AUSTRALIAN MAMMAL, AMPHIBIOUS AND OVOVIVIPAROUS... FIFTEEN LETTERS..."

WAS I OUT LONG?
NO, NO... JUST UNTIL I CAME OVER.
ARE YOU OKAY?

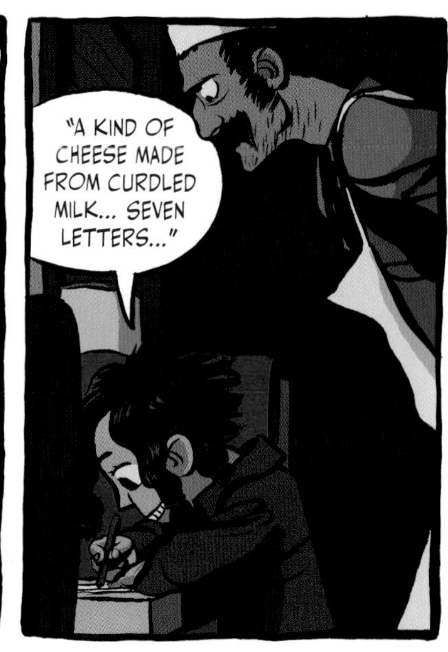
"A KIND OF CHEESE MADE FROM CURDLED MILK... SEVEN LETTERS..."

I DO THAT SOMETIMES... IT'S NOTHING...

CROSSWORD PUZZLES?
YES... AND SOMETIMES I FALL A LITTLE TOO...

SAY! IS THAT THE NUMBER OF TIMES IT'S HAPPENED?
IT'S THE SECOND BOOK.

ANYWAY, THE NOODLES ARE ON THE HOUSE...
YOU CAN EVEN HAVE A DRINK TOO!

NO! NO THANK YOU!
WHAT?

THEN YOU'LL THINK THAT I DO THIS IN EVERY RESTAURANT TO GET FREE FOOD...
NOT AT ALL, NOT AT ALL! YOU SEEM LIKE A...

IN ANY CASE, I'M GETTING YOU A DRINK!
AND NOT A WORD! PLEASE!

JULIAN, GET UP, IT WON'T WORK FOR YOU!
IN ANY CASE, YOU DON'T HAVE TO DO ANYTHING TO GET OUT OF PAYING ME!

WHAT'S YOUR NAME?

ADDIDAS...

?

BUT NOT LIKE THE SHOES, EH!

DO YOU HAVE ANY IDEAS FOR "...NO LONGER HAS A WIFE" IN SEVEN LETTERS?

THAT'S EASY! WIDOWER!

OH, YEAH, THAT WORKS... WIDOWER...
HEY! LIKE DAD...

I SHOULD HAVE THOUGHT OF THAT.

COME ON, ADDIDAS! LET'S GO!

GERMINE

SUN

WHERE IS THE COUNTRYSIDE?

THE COUNTRYSIDE?

WELL, THE COUNTRYSIDE IS PRETTY FAR... IT'S NOT NEXT DOOR...

BUT IT EXISTS?

OF COURSE IT EXISTS!
IT'S ALL AROUND...
ALL AROUND THE CITIES!

MM...

DAD?
WHAT? YOU'RE DISTRACTING ME...
IT'S DARK ENOUGH DOWN HERE !

NO, WHAT I MEANT WAS...

WHY DO THEY ALWAYS BUILD CITIES IN THE COUNTRYSIDE?

WHY?
I DON'T KNOW!
BECAUSE THERE'S NO MORE ROOM!

IT'S LIKE IN HERE... THERE'S NO MORE ROOM!

AH!

JUST A QUICK CLEANING! IF YOU PAY TOO MUCH ATTENTION TO DETAIL WE'LL BE HERE FOR WEEKS....

WHY?! I HAVE NO IDEA WHY!

SSSSH

GRRR

OÏNK

DAMN IT, ADDIDAS, THIS HAS TO STOP! YOU'RE DONE FOR THE DAY! I'LL GO TO SPENCER'S TRADE ALONE!
IT DOESN'T MATTER, I'LL FIGURE IT OUT, AND AFTERWARDS WE'RE GOING TO SEE THE DOCTOR, DAMN IT!

I THOUGHT YOU'D NEVER COME OUT...

BUT IF YOU CAN'T DO IT, MCMULLAN WILL STEAL OUR CONTRACT...
MCMULLAN! MCMULLAN!

I DON'T GIVE A SHIT ABOUT MCMULLAN! I'LL GRAB MCMULLAN LIKE THIS AND THROW HIM DOWN THE CHIMNEY!

I'M NOT GONNA LET A LITTLE SHIT TELL ME HOW TO CLEAN CHIMNEYS!

JUST BECAUSE THE MAN IS CERTIFIED DOESN'T MEAN I'M GONNA LET HIM WALK ALL OVER ME!
HAHA! LET MCMULLAN COME! I'LL TOSS HIM SO FAR DOWN HE'LL NEVER GET OUT!

WE ALREADY WENT...
WHAT?
...TO SEE THE DOCTOR.

YES, BUT LISTEN CLOSELY! WE ARE GOING TO SEE A SPECIALIST THIS TIME!
A SPECIALIST OF WHAT?

WE'LL SEE, WE'LL SEE. SPECIALISTS KNOW ALL KINDS OF THINGS, OTHERWISE THEY AREN'T SPECIALISTS!

YOU WERE DOWN THERE FOR HALF AN HOUR!
IMPOSSIBLE FOR ME TO COME AND GET YOU!
I WAS LOSING MY MIND!

IT'S NO BIG DEAL...
IT'S HAPPENED BEFORE...

I DON'T WANT TO LOSE YOU LIKE...
...LIKE YOU LOST MOM?

RIGHT? LIKE MOM?
YES!! LIKE MOM!

SHE HAD THE SAME THING?

I DON'T KNOW...
A LITTLE...

...NOT REALLY...

OH MY GOD, LOOK HOW MANY THERE ARE!
LOOK HOW MANY THERE ARE!!

WHAT THE HELL IS THIS DAMN THING?!

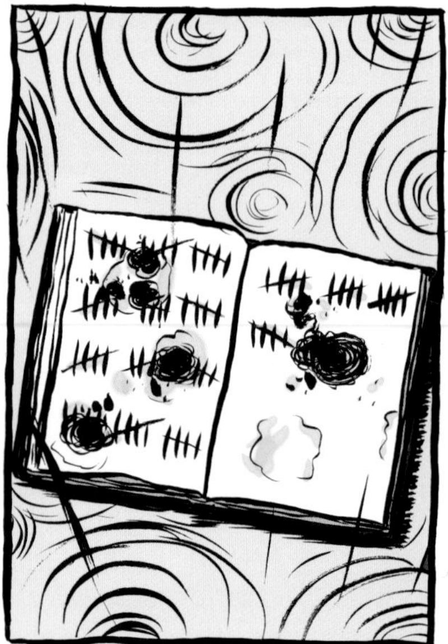

I WOULD GIVE ANYTHING TO HAVE THAT DAMN THING INSTEAD OF YOU, ADDIDAS!
ANYTHING!

COME ON, DAD, WE'LL GO TO SPENCER'S TRADE TOMORROW. THEIR CHIMNEY WON'T CLOG UP IN ONE DAY.
AND IF THEY TAKE AWAY THE CONTRACT, WELL THEN, TOO BAD!

YOU'RE SOUNDING MORE AND MORE LIKE AN ADULT...
YEAH...

NO WAY ARE YOU GOING BACK DOWN THERE!
YOU DON'T FIT IN THE SMALL FLUES, DAD.
FORGET IT...

...AND ANYWAY, I LIKE CHIMNEYS.
OUT OF THE QUESTION!

PFFF...

PFFF... WHAT PFFF?
I CAN SAY THAT TOO, PFFF...
ARE YOU A SPECIALIST OR WHAT?

IT'S DELICATE... VERY DELICATE...

IT'S UNBELIEVABLE...

PFFF... INSANE...

FOR THE LOVE OF GOD, WE DIDN'T COME HERE TO HEAR THIS!
WE MAY AS WELL HAVE GONE TO A VETERINARIAN!

HER BLACKOUTS LAST LONGER AND LONGER...
HALF AN HOUR!

YES, CALM DOWN, SIR. I AM TRYING TO MAKE A PRELIMINARY DIAGNOSIS WITH THE LITTLE INFORMATION THAT I HAVE...

I THINK WE MAY HAVE TO EXAMINE THIS FURTHER...
HMM...
...PUT HER UNDER 24-HOUR OBSERVATION.

THERE IS NOTHING ABNORMAL IN HER BLOOD, MORPHOLOGICALLY, NO GANGLIONS OR TUMORS OR VIRUSES OF ANY KIND...
TO BE HONEST, I...

...I HAVE NEVER SEEN ANYTHING LIKE IT!

I LIKE HIM!
WHAT?

NO OTHER DOCTOR ADMITTED THEY HAD NEVER SEEN ANYTHING LIKE IT... THEY ALL MADE UP STORIES:
EH, DAD?

SOME EVEN PRESCRIBED COUGH SYRUP!
HAHAHAHAHA!

YOU WERE RIGHT!
HE IS A SPECIALIST!

24-HOUR OBSERVATION...
HI HI

YES, I WOULD LIKE TO SEE WHAT HAPPENS WHEN SHE HAS AN EPISODE. WHETHER IT'S A SIMPLE BLACKOUT OR SOMETHING ELSE. I WOULD LIKE TO MONITOR HER AROUND-THE-CLOCK, AMONG OTHER THINGS, AND RUN MRIS ON HER FOR A COUPLE OF DAYS TO CHECK HER PHYSIOLOGICAL CHANGES.

I BELIEVE WE CAN FIND SOME ANSWERS...
GOOD... DO WHATEVER YOU NEED TO DO...
MY DAUGHTER CAN'T...
SHE JUST CAN'T...

HEY!!
CAN I... CAN I SPEAK TO YOU FOR A SECOND?

HOW MUCH WILL ALL OF THIS COST?
OBVIOUSLY, THESE ARE TESTS THAT REQUIRE...

tap tap tap tap tap

YES, YES. BUT HOW MUCH WILL IT ALL COST EXACTLY?

THE MACHINES, YOU UNDERSTAND, THE MACHINES ARE VERY EXPENSIVE, AND THE METHODS THAT...
JESUS CHRIST, I ASKED HOW MUCH IT WILL COST!
IS IT SUCH A COMPLICATED QUESTION?

I'M A CHIMNEY SWEEP, YOU SEE; I DON'T WORK IN FINANCE OR SPECULATION. I AM A CHIMNEY SWEEP WITH A SICK DAUGHTER! SO TELL ME WHAT I NEED TO DO TO CURE MY DAUGHTER!!

THERE ARE WAYS... I...
IT IS QUITE EXPENSIVE, YES...

IT'S QUITE EXPENSIVE...

SSLURRP...

ZZZZ...

SHE WAS TALL AND THIN, LIKE A SPRIG...
YES!!

BUT NOT FRAIL! DON'T THINK THAT! OTHERWISE SHE NEVER WOULD HAVE... I NEVER WOULD HAVE BROUGHT HER WITH ME... TO WORK.

LOOK HOW...

LOOK! GOD, ISN'T SHE BEAUTIFUL!

IN THIS JOB, YOU NEED SMALL PEOPLE... SMALL PEOPLE FOR SMALL FLUES...
OTHERWISE YOU CAN'T GET WORK...

SSLUURRP...

IT'S AS IF YOU WERE SENDING YOUR KID TO THE BOTTOM OF YOUR GLASS THERE! YOU GODDAMN...
WE HAVE TO GO HOME NOW.

WH... WHAT?!

WE'RE GOING TO THE COUNTRYSIDE...
WE'RE GOING HOME...

I SAID WE'RE GOING TO THE COUNTRYSIDE... I MAKE THE RULES!
I'M YOUR FATHER!

HOP
COME ON...

IT'S THIS WAY...

HUH?

...OR MAYBE THAT WAY...

NO... IT'S DOWN HERE...

WELL...
I WAS SURE IT WAS THIS WAY...

WE HAVE TO GO HOME, DAD. MCMULLAN IS GOING TO STEAL OUR CONTRACT...
MCMULLAN, MCMULLAN!
I DON'T GIVE A SHIT ABOUT MCMULLAN!

HE BETTER NOT COME INTO MY CHIMNEY, 'CAUSE I'LL BURY HIM IN THE BOTTOM!
OUT OF SIGHT, OUT OF MIND!
HAHA!

PFFF...

I WOULD HAVE LOVED TO HAVE SHOWN YOU THE COUNTRYSIDE...
...'CAUSE THE COUNTRYSIDE'S NICE...

POC

WONDER

DAD?

ZZZZ...
MMPH...
RRRZZZ...

CRAK

?!
SSSSSSSH

PSSSSH

YOU OKAY, KID?

?!

WHAT THE HELL ARE YOU DOING HERE?!

THIS IS MY CONTRACT! MINE AND MY FATHER'S!

NOT ANYMORE! YOU SHOULD HAVE DONE IT YESTERDAY!
THE SPENCERS DON'T TAKE KINDLY TO THESE KINDS OF SHENANIGANS!

GO ON! FAIR IS FAIR... GO BACK UP THERE AND TELL YOUR FATHER TO GET OUT OF HERE!

NO!

WHAT?
IT'S OUR CONTRACT!

IT'S WRITTEN HERE!
"SPENCER'S TRADE"!

HMM...

TELL ME, YOU LITTLE SQUIRT... WHERE *IS* YOUR DADDY?

IF YOU WANT TO STAY, THEN STAY!
WHATEVER YOUR FATHER DOESN'T DO, I TAKE! IT'S THE LAW! THE DISTRICT BELONGS TO BOTH OF US!

OHHH, LOOK HERE! IT APPEARS THAT "JIM'S PAWN SHOP" NEEDS A LITTLE CLEANING TOO!

WE'LL GO TAKE A LOOK AFTER THIS!
YEAH!
HEH HEH

HEH HEH HEH HEH HEH HEH...

HA HA HA HA HA HA HA
HEH HEH HEH HEH HEH HEH...

HA HA HA HA HA HA HA HA
HA HA HA HA HA HA HA

HAVE ANY MORE LITTLE PAPERS LIKE THIS ONE?

YOU'RE DISGUSTING!
YOU'RE A CONTRACT STEALER AND A BIG UGLY PIG!

AND MY FATHER SAID THAT HE WOULD TOSS YOU INTO THE BOTTOM!

tap tap

HE ALREADY THREW YOUR MOTHER DOWN THERE! WASN'T THAT ENOUGH FOR HIM?

GODDAMN IT, GO! GO AND GET HER, YOU IDIOT!

SNIFF...

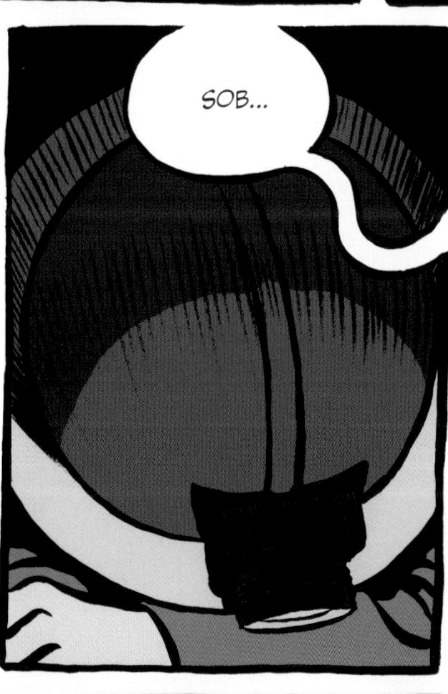
SOB...

?
SNIFF...

SOB...

SNIFF...

ZIP

AAAAAHH!

SNIFF...
SOB...
IS SOMEONE
THERE?
SNI...

?!

ARE YOU REAL?

WHY ARE YOU CRYING?
ARE YOU AFRAID?

DON'T BE!

NO... THIS IS JUST CHIMNEY SOOT...

AH...

04.03. FREDERIK-WAZEM

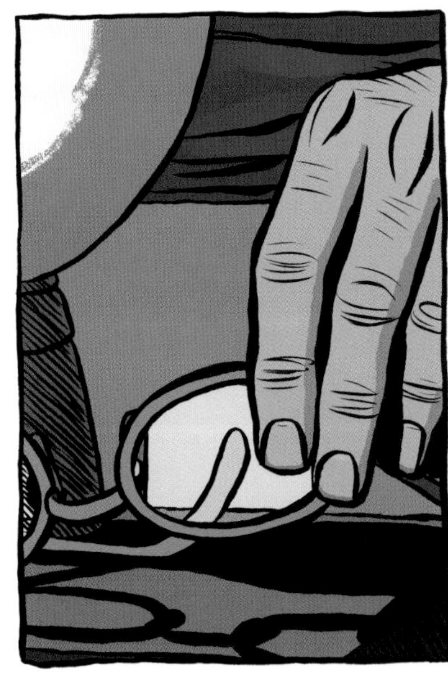

GRAT

FOR THE LOVE OF GOD!

ADDIDAS!

FOR THE LOVE OF GOD!

THE BAG!
THE TOOLS!

ADDIDAS!
SLAM!!

I TOLD HER NOT TO GO ALONE!
I TOLD HER NOT TO GO AT ALL!

JESUS CHRIST, SHE WAS NEVER SUPPOSED TO GO BACK INTO ANOTHER CHIMNEY!

SPENCER'S
TRADE

WHAT THE HELL ARE YOU TWO DOING THERE?!
WHERE IS ADDIDAS?

YOU HAVE NO BUSINESS HERE, THIS IS MY CONTRACT!
ADDIDAS!

INDEED.
WHAT?!

INDEED...
THE LITTLE ONE'S ALREADY UP THERE...

AH, GOOD! GOOD GIRL! GET OUT OF MY WAY, FOR CHRIST'S SAKE!
GOOD JOB, ADDIDAS! HAHAHA! YOU WANT TO STEAL OUR CONTRACT, EH?!

ACTUALLY, I MEAN, SHE'S IN THERE...
SHE ALREADY STARTED?
GOOD... GOOD...

UH... YEAH...
... ACTUALLY ...

...MMMM...
SHE'LL BE OUT SOON...

GET THE HELL OUT OF HERE! YOU HAVE NO BUSINESS HERE!
OUCH!

ADDIDAS! COME UP!
I'M HERE! IT'S DADDY!

ADDIDAAAS!
HELLLOOOO...

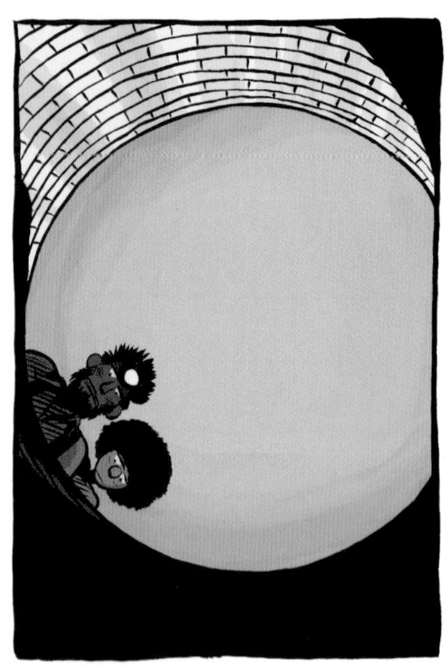

WHAT THE HELL ARE YOU TWO STILL DOING HERE?

ACTUALLY, YOUR DAUGHTER... I THINK SHE MAY BE A LITTLE ANGRY...

ANGRY?!

I TOLD HER ABOUT YOUR WIFE. THAT YOU... I MEAN, THAT SHE STAYED DOWN THERE...
I THOUGHT SHE KNEW THE STORY...

CHRIST, I DIDN'T MEAN TO...

YOU BASTARD!
YOU GODDAMN BASTARD!

AH!

AAAH...
YOU! GO AND FIND HER!

I ALREADY WENT...

...BUT I COULDN'T FIND HER...

WHAT? COULDN'T FIND HER? DID YOU GO TO THE BOTTOM?!

OF COURSE! BUT THERE WAS NO ONE!

NO ONE...

WHY ARE YOU HERE?
AND WHY ARE YOU CRYING?

BROKE MACHINE...
YOU BROKE THE MACHINE? WHICH ONE?

...MINE...

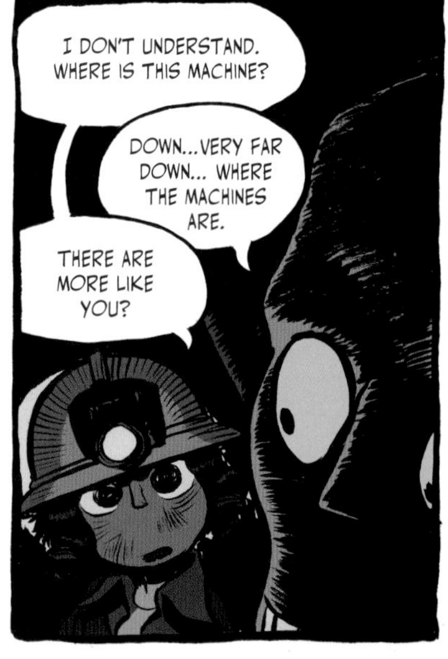
I DON'T UNDERSTAND. WHERE IS THIS MACHINE?
DOWN...VERY FAR DOWN... WHERE THE MACHINES ARE.
THERE ARE MORE LIKE YOU?

AM I DEAD?
DON'T KNOW... NEVER SAW REALS... ONLY MACHINES...
REAL WHAT?

LIKE YOU...

WELL, I'VE NEVER SEEN ANY...ANYTHING LIKE YOU...
AND WHO CAN TALK TOO...

SHOW ME YOUR MACHINES...

NO, NO... I BROKE... I BROKE...
WE CAN'T FIX IT?

I SAID COME ON!
YOUR MACHINE SOUNDS INTERESTING!

WHAT ARE YOU DOING HERE? YOU... IMPOSSIBLE THAT THE REALS COME HERE!
OH, YEAH?
WELL, I'M A CHIMNEY SWEEP AND I SLID AND I'M GLAD 'CAUSE I NEVER WANT TO GO BACK UP THERE!

WHY?

WE DON'T KNOW EACH OTHER WELL ENOUGH TO DISCUSS THAT.

OH, YEAH, ONE THING: SOMETIMES I FALL DOWN FOR A BIT. JUST WAIT IT OUT, IT'S NO BIG DEAL. IT'S A SICKNESS.
A VERY SPECIAL SICKNESS.

YOU DON'T EAT LITTLE GIRLS, DO YOU?

OH NO, WE DON'T EAT THE REALS.
WE ONLY TAKE CARE OF THEIR MACHINES.
GOOD!
I'M ADDIDAS EME BY THE WAY... WHAT'S YOUR NAME?

ADDIDAS?!
YEAH...

MACHINE'S NAME ADDIDAS TOO...
BUT NOT "EME."
REALLY? I THOUGHT IT WAS THE WHATCHAMACALLIT MACHINE...

THAT TOO.
MACHINES HAVE HUMAN NAMES?

YES. THE HUMAN'S NAME... EACH MACHINE, ONE HUMAN...
EXACTLY!

YOU BROKE IT?
NEVER... WORKED... RIGHT...

WAS IT SICK?
YES.

SO, IT'S A LITTLE LIKE ME...

SHOW ME THIS MACHINE!
NO, NO... NO GO DOWN.

COME ON, I SAID! IN ANY CASE, I AM NOT GOING BACK UP THERE!

350012

COMMISSIONER!
COMMISSIONER!

WAIT YOUR TURN!
BUT IT'S NOT ABOUT ME! IT'S MY DAUGHTER!

WHAT ARE YOU DOING THEN? BRING YOUR DAUGHTER!
SHE FELL INTO THE BOTTOM OF A CHIMNEY!

SHE'S STUCK AT THE BOTTOM OF A CHIMNEY!
ARGGHH
HEY!
OH!

NAME?

EME.
"M"?
NO, NOT "M," EME!

STRANGE!

YES, IT'S THE ADMINISTRATION'S FAULT.
REALLY?
YES, MY REAL NAME IS ARRE, JULIUS ARRE... BUT IT DIDN'T FIT WITH THE MACHINES' FILES, SO THEY CHANGED IT TO EME.

STRANGE...
FROT
FROT

IT'S NOT STRANGE! WHAT'S STRANGE IS THAT I AM STANDING HERE CHATTING WITH YOU WHILE MY DAUGHTER IS STUCK AT THE BOTTOM OF A CHIMNEY! MY NAME IS JULIUS EME, OKAY? NOW LET'S GO AND GET MY DAUGHTER!

YOU NEED TO CALM DOWN! YOU WON'T GET HER BACK BY GETTING WORKED UP. AND ANYWAY, I FIND YOU IRRESPONSIBLE! NORMAL PEOPLE DON'T LET THEIR DAUGHTERS PLAY IN CHIMNEYS!

SHE WASN'T PLAYING FOR CHRIST'S SAKE! SHE WAS WORKING! SHE'S A CHIMNEY SWEEP! SHE HELPS ME WITH THE SMALL FLUES!

SHE HELPS YOU? YOUR OWN DAUGHTER? SOUNDS SHADY...

WHAT DO YOU MEAN "SHADY"? SHADY HOW?
WE HAVE LAMPS, SIR... WE WORK WITH LAMPS...

FOR THE LOVE OF GOD, LET'S GO, WE HAVE TO GET HER OUT OF THERE!
SO, JULIUS EME...
CERTIFIED CHIMNEY SWEEP?

I...
I'M A CHIMNEY SWEEP... YES.

CERTIFIED?

NO, NO, NOT CERTIFIED... WE DO WHAT WE CAN, EH...TO MAKE A LIVING! BUT IT DOESN'T CHANGE THE FACT THAT MY DAUGHTER IS STUCK. WE CAN TAKE CARE OF THAT LATER. LET'S GO AND GET MY DAUGHTER!
NOT CERTIFIED AND YOU DARE COME HERE, INTO MY HEADQUARTERS!

JOKER, I'VE SMOKED YOU OUT!

HA HA HA HA HA HA HA HA HA HA HA

HAHA
DID YOU HEAR THAT?! "I'VE SMOKED YOU OUT!" ... HE'S A CHIMNEY SWEEP!!!
HAHAHAHAHA!

HMM...

DO WHATEVER YOU WANT TO ME... JUST GET MY DAUGHTER OUT!

YOUR NAILS ARE DISGUSTING!

PUT HIM WITH THE OTHERS FOR THE PIT! HE HAS HANDS FOR DIGGING AND HE'S NOT CERTIFIED! IDIOT'S NOT REGISTERED ANYWHERE!

BUT?!

AND THE DAUGHTER?
?
I COULD NOT CARE LESS ABOUT THE DAUGHTER!

SHE'S IN A CHIMNEY, FINE!
I WANTED TO BE A FLAMENCO DANCER AND I'M A COMMISSIONER!

I DON'T CARE ABOUT THE DAUGHTER!
LET GO OF ME!

CLAC:

HOLD ON! GET OUT OF THERE, ADDIDAS! YOU'RE CLEVER; YOU CAN GET OUT OF THERE... IT'S NOT YOUR FIRST CHIMNEY...

VROOM

WHERE ARE WE GOING?
DOES ANYONE KNOW?

WE'RE GOING TO THE PIT...
I'VE BEEN TWICE ALREADY.

ARE WE GOING TO DIE?
OF COURSE NOT... WE DIG, THAT'S ALL.

WE DIG?
YEAH, WE DIG... THEY THINK THERE'S SOMETHING AT THE BOTTOM.

ARE WE GOING TO DIG FOR A LONG TIME?
I HAVE A FAMILY...
IT DEPENDS...

ON WHAT?

IT DEPENDS...

MY GOD. CAN'T YOU BE A LITTLE CLEARER? IT DEPENDS ON WHAT, HE ASKED?!

I DON'T KNOW, REALLY. THERE'S NO LOGIC TO IT.
SOME WILL DIG THEIR WHOLE LIVES...

I DON'T WANT TO DIG! I DON'T WANT TO DIG ANYTHING!

I'M IN ADMINISTRATION, THERE'S BEEN A MISTAKE! A TERRIBLE MISTAKE!
I'VE NEVER DUG ANYTHING! NOT EVEN THE TINIEST HOLE!

WELL, YOU WON'T BE DISAPPOINTED! BECAUSE HOLES LIKE THIS...

...YOU'VE NEVER SEEN ANYTHING LIKE IT!

IT'S DISGUSTING!
EAT! YOU'D BETTER EAT! YOU GET ONLY ONE PER DAY!

I'D RATHER EAT ROCKS...
YOU'LL EAT SOME OF THOSE ANYWAY!

GREAT...
YEAH...

WHY DON'T YOU WANT TO SEE YOUR FRIENDS?

WHEN BREAK MACHINE, WE HAVE TO LEAVE WITH IT...
THAT SUCKS!

HERE IS LIKE THAT...

YEAH WELL, IT STILL SUCKS!

IT'S PRETTY STRANGE WHERE YOU LIVE...

CROINK

?

PSST...

HAVE AN EXTRA ONE?

DO YOU KNOW WHY WE'RE DIGGING?

NO, THEY FOUND SOMETHING DOWN THERE, I THINK...
WELL, THEY THINK THEY FOUND SOMETHING...
IT MUST BE HUGE!

I SHOULD QUIT...
DIGGING?
CIGARETTES.

HUH?
YEAH, IT'S NOT GOOD FOR YOUR HEALTH.

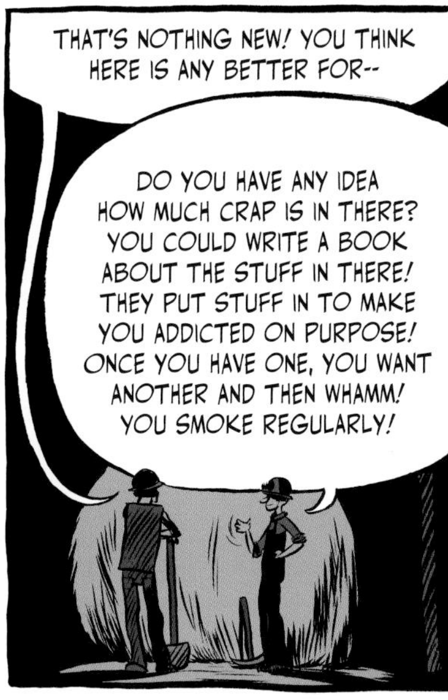
THAT'S NOTHING NEW! YOU THINK HERE IS ANY BETTER FOR--
DO YOU HAVE ANY IDEA HOW MUCH CRAP IS IN THERE? YOU COULD WRITE A BOOK ABOUT THE STUFF IN THERE! THEY PUT STUFF IN TO MAKE YOU ADDICTED ON PURPOSE! ONCE YOU HAVE ONE, YOU WANT ANOTHER AND THEN WHAMM! YOU SMOKE REGULARLY!

EVER THOUGHT OF THAT?

I THINK ABOUT IT ALL THE TIME...
SEE, SEE?! WHAT DID I TELL YOU?!

AND THEY DON'T MAKE THEM WITH HEALTHY INGREDIENTS! I DON'T KNOW...LIKE APPLES FOR INSTANCE! YOU EAT ONE THEN YOU COULDN'T CARE LESS ABOUT THEM! ANYONE EVER ASK YOU FOR AN APPLE?
I WOULD GLADLY EAT THAT APPLE!

I'M TELLING YOU! IT'S KILLING US!
AND I CAN'T... I HAVE TO FIND MY DAUGHTER!
THINK ABOUT IT! YOU SHOULD QUIT!

WELL, ANYWAYS, WE'LL DIE HERE ALMOST AS QUICKLY AS WE'LL DIE FROM SMOKING! OPEN YOURS EYES, NO ONE LEAVES HERE ALIVE!
SMOKER OR NOT...

ARE YOU CRAZY?
I'M GETTING OUT OF HERE...

I'M LIKE THE SMOKE...
I ALWAYS FIND A WAY OUT...

DON'T WORRY ABOUT ME. GO! I WON'T LOSE TWO DOWN THERE... NO WAY!

BROMBROLOMBROM

SHHHH!

THAT'S STRANGE...
...IT IS STILL WORKING.
YOU SEE, ALL IS NOT LOST!

"AD-DID-AS"
"AR-RE"

WHAT DID YOU SAY?
MY MACHINE...
ADDIDAS ARRE?

IT'S MY REAL...
HE MUST BE DYING...

THAT'S MY NAME...
BUT... BUT I THOUGHT THAT?!...

THEN... YOU... YOU SHOULD BE DEAD!

WELL, WHAT DID I SAY?! I KNEW YOU DIDN'T EXIST IN THE REAL WORLD...
IMPOSSIBLE!
MACHINE IS WITH THE BROKEN MACHINES! MACHINE NOT EVEN PLUGGED IN!

THAT SUCKS FOR DAD NOW. HE'S ALL ALONE AND WON'T HAVE ANYONE FOR THE SMALL FLUES...
IF ONLY HE HAD TOLD ME THE TRUTH ABOUT MOM...
WE WOULDN'T BE HERE...

POOR DAD...
DEATH IS PRETTY STRANGE...
I'M THE ONE WHO'S SAD FOR HIM...

YOU NOT UNDERSTAND... YOU ARE NOT DEAD!

NO?
NO.

IT'S BETTER IN A WAY, I GUESS...

BUT YOU SHOULD BE...

I SHOULD BE?
OKAY...

IT'S POSSIBLE THEN.
HOW DOES IT WORK?

QUESTION OF BALANCE... NOT TOO MUCH HERE... NOT TOO MUCH THERE...

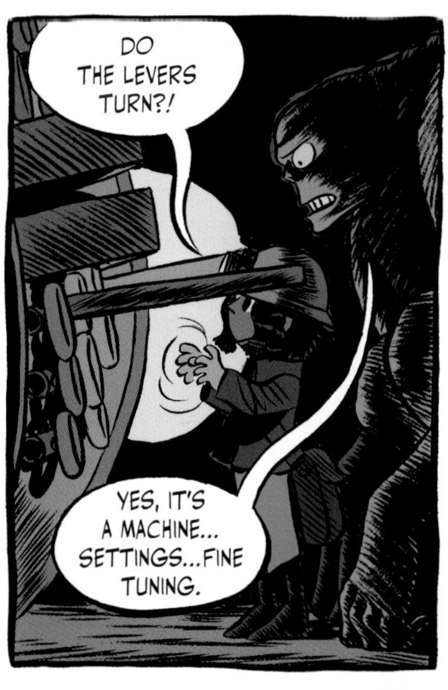
DO THE LEVERS TURN?!
YES, IT'S A MACHINE... SETTINGS...FINE TUNING.

YOU DON'T SAY...

CAN I TURN THESE?
NO... NO...

COME ON! IT'S MINE AFTER ALL!
AND APPARENTLY IT DOESN'T WORK LIKE YOU THINK IT DOES SINCE I SHOULD BE DEAD!

NO! YOU SHOULDN'T TOUCH! NO TOUCH MACHINE! NOT ONE LEVER! NOTHING!

NO TOUCH!

SAY, YOU DON'T HAVE SPECIALISTS HERE?

SPECIALISTS LIKE WE HAVE UP THERE?
WHO DON'T KNOW MUCH BUT TRY TO FIND OUT?

MAYBE...
SOMEONE WHO MIGHT KNOW WHY I'M SICK UP THERE AND ALIVE DOWN HERE?

THIS MACHINE WAS ALWAYS ODD...
WELL, *THANKS A LOT!*

AAAAHH!
?

LISTEN, ASSHOLE! THIS IS YOUR LAST CHANCE TO STAY ALIVE! JUST DO YOUR JOB AND DIG. IF YOU TRY TO ESCAPE AGAIN, YOU DIE!
AHHH...

THUMP
YOU'RE AN IDIOT, OLD MAN! ONLY IDIOTS HAVE HOPE HERE, DON'T YOU GET IT?

OUCH...

WHAT THE HELL ARE YOU DOING HERE?

SAME AS YOU...
WHAT... YOU'RE NOT CERTIFIED?

NO, ACTUALLY, I'M NOT...
HAHA, SWINDLER!
OUCH!

AND THE KID?
HE GOT AWAY...
HE WENT TO GET YOUR KID AND NEVER CAME BACK UP EITHER... I YELLED FOR HOURS!

IMPOSSIBLE!
DID YOU COMPLAIN?!
AS YOU CAN SEE...

SHOULD NEVER COMPLAIN, HUH?...

HA HA HA HA HA HA HA HA HA HA HA

WE'LL GET OUT OF HERE!
WE'LL FIND THEM!

SEEMS THEY SEND THE INJURED BACK... THEY CAN'T DIG ANYMORE...

WITH A BROKEN LEG, WE CAN'T DIG ANYMORE, RIGHT?
CAN YOU BREAK MY LEG?
SHIT! I DON'T KNOW!

JUMP RIGHT THERE, IN THE MIDDLE!

JESUS CHRIST, ARE YOU CRAZY?!
JUMP, I SAID!

HOW DO YOU KNOW THEY WON'T KILL YOU?
HE SAID IT.
WELL, THAT'S WHAT I HEARD...

CAN'T DIG WITH A BROKEN HAND, RIGHT?
HOW CAN WE BREAK OUR HAND?
YOU'RE ALL CRAZY!

THEY'LL KILL ALL OF YOU, BROKEN HAND OR NO BROKEN HAND! SO, BREAK WHATEVER YOU WANT, YOU'LL ALL BE DEAD MEN ANYWAY! DEAD BROKEN MEN BUT DEAD NONETHELESS!

THINK IT'LL HURT?

LOOK WHAT I'M DOING SINCE NO ONE WILL BREAK MY LEG...
...I'M GOING TO MAKE A BOULDER FALL ON IT!

??
POC POC

YUP, I'M CHISELING IT SO THAT ONE DAY SOON ALL IT NEEDS IS ONE GOOD PICK AND WHAP! ON MY LEG! AND UP I GO!

I'LL HIT IT HERE, LIKE THIS, AND IT WILL TOPPLE THERE!

ARE YOU NUTS...

YOUR LEG WILL BE CRUSHED!
NO, NO... JUST BROKEN... YOU'LL SEE...

SO, WE ALL HAVE A MACHINE LIKE THIS?

YES, YES... CONNECTED...
SO, DAD HAS ONE TOO?

OF COURSE... NOT FAR FROM YOURS...
AH... YOU KNOW WHERE IT IS THEN?
YES, I KNOW...

SO, WE'LL CHANGE A COUPLE OF THINGS ON DAD'S AND THEN I'LL GO BACK UP...

CAN WE CHANGE THINGS ON A NORMAL PERSON?
DIFFICULT... CHANGE... BALANCED...

I JUST WANT TO MAX HIS SWITCH FOR "LOVE." THAT WAY HE'LL STOP CRYING WHEN HE LOOKS AT MOM'S PICTURE AND HE'LL STOP DRINKING AND HE'LL MEET A NICE LADY AND EVERYTHING WILL BE PERFECT.

LOVE?
WHAT? NO LEVER FOR LOVE?
NO.
FINE! WE'LL SEE...

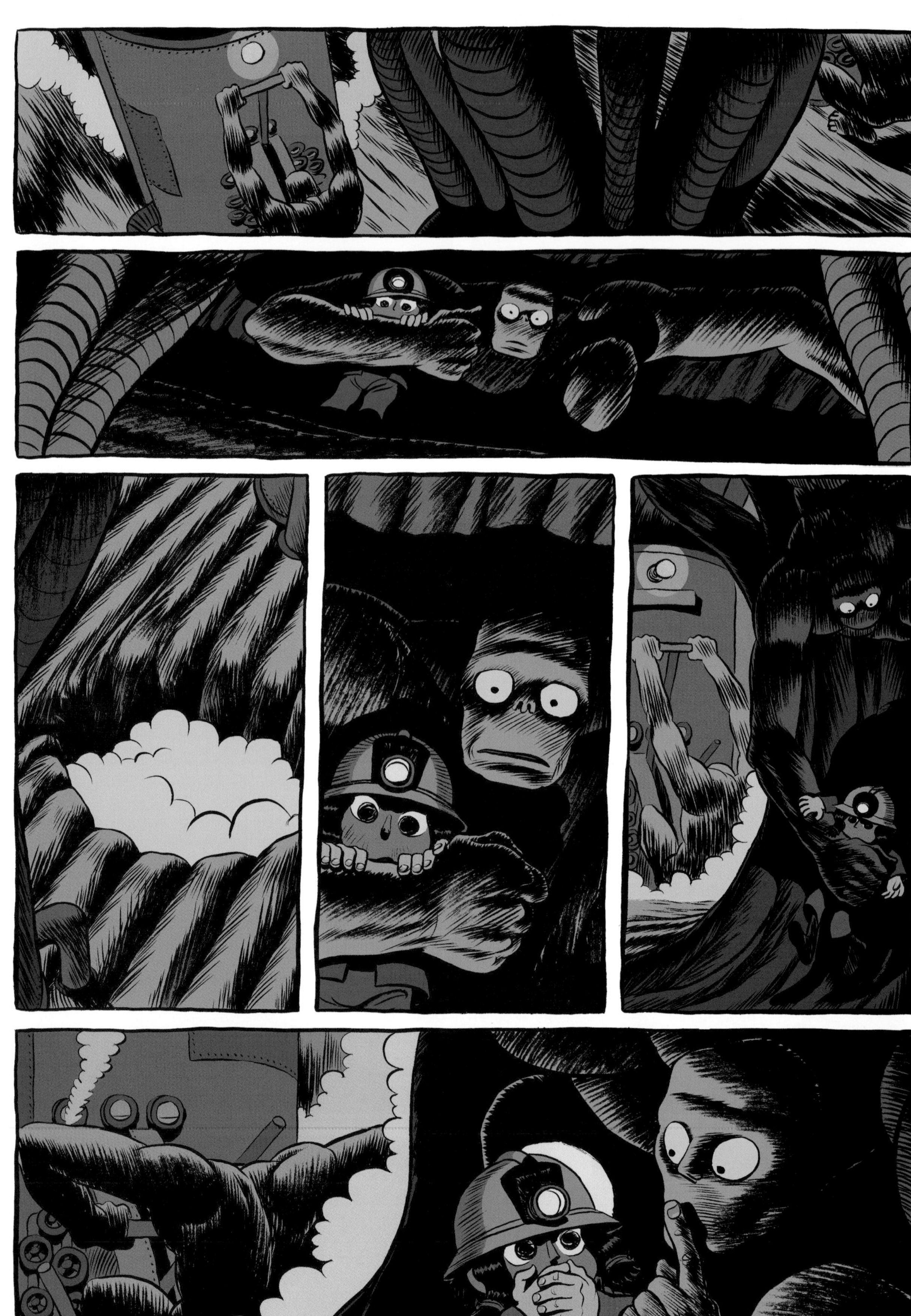

WE HAVE TO WAIT UNTIL SLEEP...
WHEN DAD IS SLEEPING?
YES...

HE MUST NOT BE SLEEPING VERY WELL RIGHT NOW BECAUSE HE MUST BE WORRIED ABOUT ME...

HE WILL SLEEP, IT IS REQUIRED...

HG
TUNNEL! ISIDIRO.
POLIKARPOV.
EVANS.

ARTUR.
ISAPJORDHUR.
LATHESE.

EME...

THAT IS NOT MY TUNNEL!
WHY ARE YOU--

MMMPH...

FOR THE LOVE OF GOD, THAT'S NOT MY TUNNEL! I'VE SPENT HOURS ON THAT BOULDER! IT'S GOING TO GET RUINED!
WILL YOU SHUT UP?!

TAKE MY PLACE! TAKE MY PLACE, THEY WON'T EVEN NOTICE!
ARE YOU CRAZY?!

JULIUS
EME!

TAKE MY PLACE! AFTER ALL, IT'S YOUR FAULT THAT I'M HERE!
DAMN YOU!

YES.
JULIUS EME...

MOVE IT, FOR CHRIST'S SAKE!

B TUNNEL...

MACKINGLEY. MULLER.
SINUS.

FLANHAGGAN.
BULL.

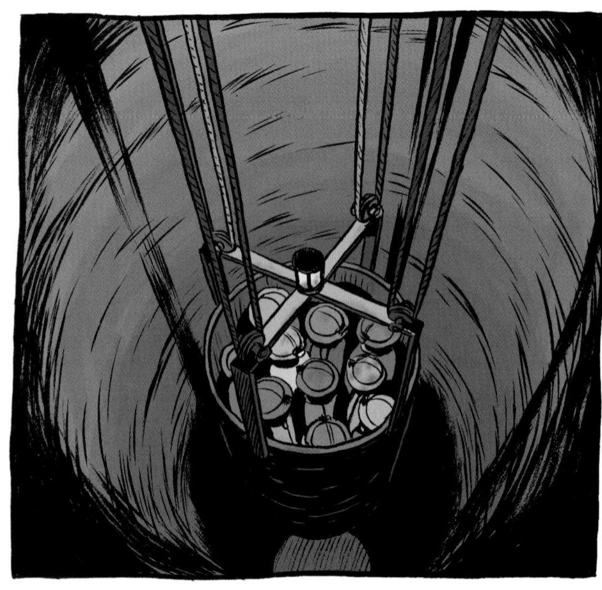

PTOO...

POUF

POUF
POUF

AAAAHH!

HEY, ANYONE HERE?

ADDIDAS?

ADDIDAS, QUIT MESSING AROUND!
IF YOU'RE THERE, ANSWER!

AH!

AAAAHH!

AAAAAAAAAAA

AAAAAAAAA

GNNN!
GNNIIIH!

PAF

CLIC

I MOVED MY LEG...

FOR CHRIST'S SAKE, I MOVED MY LEG AT THE LAST SECOND!

THE BOULDER FELL PERFECTLY!
MY TICKET OUT OF HERE!

AND I MOVED MY LEG...

IT'S FUNNY HOW YOU CAN'T THINK OF ONE THING WITHOUT THINKING OF ANOTHER.

I'M WONDERING WHEN OUR WORRIES KEEP US FROM SLEEPING, IF IT HAPPENS LITTLE BY LITTLE...
BUT ALSO ABOUT AT WHAT EXACT HEIGHT A HILL BECOMES A MOUNTAIN...

AND HOW MY MOTHER WAS AND HOW MY FATHER WAS WITH HER WHEN THEY WERE JUST THE TWO OF THEM...

CAN WE FIND MY MOTHER'S MACHINE AT THE MACHINE CEMETERY?

CEMETERY MACHINES DESTROYED TO MAKE OTHER MACHINES...

WHAT ABOUT MINE?
YOURS NOT LET BE DESTROYED!
FIND SOLUTION...

OKAY...

I THINK A LOT ABOUT THAT...

NOT LIKE YOU...

03.04. FREDERIK – WAZEM

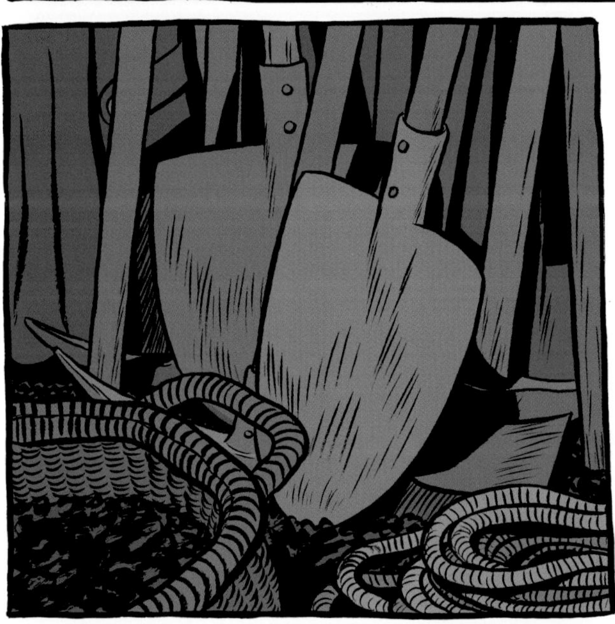

ADDIDAS!

ADDIDAS?

MMM?
YOUR DAD IS SLEEPING.

AH.

SAD ABOUT YOUR MOM.

YOU KNOW THE STORY?
YOU LOOKED AFTER MY MOTHER'S MACHINE?

NO. ONE MACHINE, ONE HUMAN, ONE LIKE ME.
YOU SPEAK TO EACH OTHER. THOSE...THOSE LIKE YOU?

YOU TALK WHILE SLEEP.

I SEE.

NOTHING YOUR FATHER COULD HAVE DONE.
YES, THAT'S LIFE. NOTHING WE CAN DO, RIGHT?

ACTUALLY, I THINK THAT'S LIFE BUT I DON'T REALLY KNOW FOR SURE. I GUESS THAT'S LIFE OR SOMETHING LIKE THAT.
OKAY, SO EXPLAIN A LITTLE ABOUT HOW THIS WORKS?

COMPLICATED.
QUESTION OF BALANCE.
COMPLICATED.

YOUR DAD NOT GOOD.
HE'S NOT OKAY?
NOT GOOD.

HE'S WORRIED.
IT'S NORMAL.
I'VE BEEN GONE FOR A BIT ALREADY.

toc toc

MORE THAN WORRIED.
SAD.
MAD.
TIRED.
DISCOURAGED.

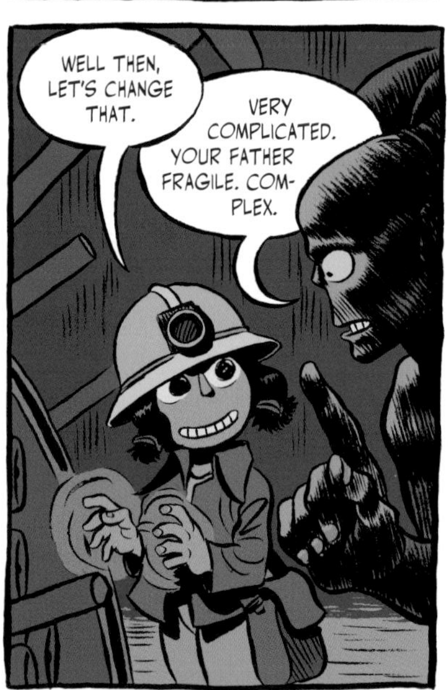
WELL THEN, LET'S CHANGE THAT.
VERY COMPLICATED. YOUR FATHER FRAGILE. COMPLEX.

CAN I SPEAK TO HIM?

WHAT?

SPEAK TO HIM.
LIKE ON A TELEPHONE, SORT OF!

YOU...TRY.

LIFT ME UP.

tap
tap

DAD...
CAN YOU HEAR ME?

DAD, IT'S ME!

DRRRING

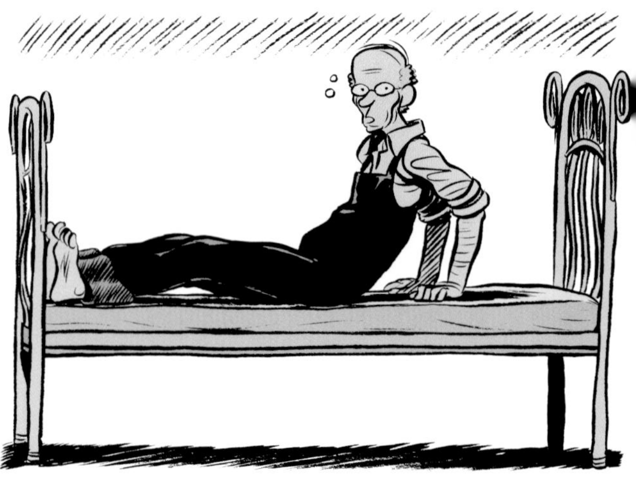

DRRRRRiiiiiiNG!..

HELLO?

DAD?

HELLO?
DAD, CAN YOU HEAR ME?

ADDIDAS?
I'M HERE, CAN YOU HEAR ME?
HELLO?

THERE'S SOMETHING WRONG WITH THE CONNECTION.

IT'S ME! IT'S ADDIDAS! ARE YOU STILL THERE?
ADDIDAS, IS THAT YOU?
I'M HERE!
MY GOD! WHERE ARE YOU?

AND...
WHERE AM I?

I'LL EXPLAIN LATER. DAD, YOU HAVE TO TELL ME WHAT'S WRONG. I'M STANDING IN FRONT OF YOUR MACHINE. I CAN FIX EVERYTHING.

WHAT ARE YOU TALKING ABOUT? I CAN HEAR YOU AS IF YOU WERE RIGHT HERE.
THAT'S NORMAL. CAN YOU PLEASE LISTEN FOR ONE SECOND?
OF COURSE!

YOU HAVE TO TELL ME WHAT'S WRONG.
???
DAD?
YES. YES.

YOU HAVE TO TELL ME.
IN WHAT WAY?

YOUR MACHINE IS NOT WORKING PROPERLY. IT'S SAD AND...
MAD.
AND MAD AND EVERYTHING.

WHO IS THERE WITH YOU?
I HEARD SOMEONE!

ARE YOU WITH...?
I DON'T HAVE TIME TO EXPLAIN. DAD, WHAT'S WRONG? TELL ME QUICKLY, I DON'T KNOW HOW LONG THIS CONNECTION WILL LAST...

MY GOD, ADDIDAS, NOTHING IS GOING RIGHT!
I'M LOCKED UP IN THIS PIT DIGGING ROCKS WHEN I SHOULD BE OUT SEARCHING HEAVEN AND EARTH FOR YOU.
WHERE ARE YOU CALLING ME FROM?
YOU'RE IN A PIT?

WHERE IS THIS PIT? I AM COMING TO GET YOU, DAD.
BUT, WHERE THE HELL ARE YOU? AND HOW DID YOU GET THIS...THIS NUMBER?
LATER! WHERE IS THIS PIT?

I HAVE NO IDEA.
THE AUTHORI-TIES KNOW.
THE POLICE DEPARTMENT SENT ME HERE.
OKAY.
OKAY?!?

DAD?
WHAT?
DAD, I'M NOT MAD AT YOU FOR WHAT HAPPENED TO MOM.
THERE WAS NOTHING YOU COULD DO.

I'M HANGING UP NOW.
ADDIDAS?
THIS IS A DREAM, ISN'T IT?
I HAVE TO GO NOW.

NO!
DON'T HANG UP. DON'T HANG UP.
I HAVE TO GO.
I LOVE YOU, DAD.

WE HAVE TO GO AND GET MY FATHER.
WE HAVE TO GO BACK.

NEVER GONE UP.
NOW'S THE TIME.
I'LL NEED YOU.
THERE'S A PIT AND HE'S INSIDE DIGGING.

AND YOUR MACHINE.
VERY DANGEROUS.
YOUR MACHINE ALMOST DEAD.
WE'LL WORRY ABOUT THAT LATER. ANYWAY, IT'S FINE WHERE IT IS, THERE'S NO RISK OF DANGER.

BUT BEFORE THAT, YOU'RE GOING TO FIDDLE WITH THE LEVERS AND GIVE MY FATHER SOME COURAGE.
COURAGE AND STRENGTH.
HE HAS TO STAY STRONG UNTIL WE GET THERE.

FRAGILE...
YOU ALREADY SAID THAT.
WHAT IS THE POINT OF THESE MACHINES IF WE CAN'T DO ANYTHING WITH THEM?

QUESTION OF BALAN...
YOU ALREADY SAID THAT.
TURN THE HANDLES.
TURN MY FATHER INTO A SUPERHERO!

???

SUPERHERO?
SUPER STRONG, YOU KNOW!

COURAGE AND STRENGTH.
CLIC
DANGEROUS.

WE'LL COME BACK AND MAKE SOME ADJUSTMENTS.
WE HAVE TO FIND THE WAY UP. WE HAVE TO GO TO THE POLICE DEPARTMENT!

POLICE DEPARTMENT?
YEAH, IT'S A...
SOME PLACE.

POUF

MMM...

I SPOKE TO MY DAUGHTER ON THE PHONE. I SPOKE TO MY DAUGHTER ON THE PHONE!

??

ON THE PHONE?
ON THE PHONE!

MMM-HMM.
AND WHERE'S THIS PHONE?
WELL, RIGHT HERE...

YUP.
YEAH.

IT WAS...
IT REALLY HAPPENED.
REALLY?
YOU ACTUALLY THINK THEY'D HAVE A PHONE BOOTH HERE?
ONE PER SLEEPING QUARTER, I GUESS. AND WE WOULD ALL HAVE A DIRECT LINE. SO WE CAN CHAT WITH OUR FAMILY ONCE IN A WHILE, ORDER PIZZA AND BEER...

DON'T WORRY, IT'S NORMAL. WE JUST NEED TO KEEP OUR FEET ON THE GROUND.
OR UNDER-GROUND, SO TO SPEAK.
I REFUSE TO LEAVE MY FEET HERE.

IT WAS A PREMONITION!
A SIGN!
A SIGN!

JULIUS, GO BACK TO SLEEP. WE HAVE TO BE UP IN TWO HOURS!
CAN'T YOU SEE YOU'VE GOT IT ALL WRONG?

WRONG? WHAT?
AND I GUESS WE'RE RIGHT AND...REAL? AND IF IT DID ME GOOD TO BELIEVE THAT SHE PHONED ME WHILE I WAS SLEEPING, SO WHAT? I DON'T WANT TO SLEEP.
I FEEL ALIVE!

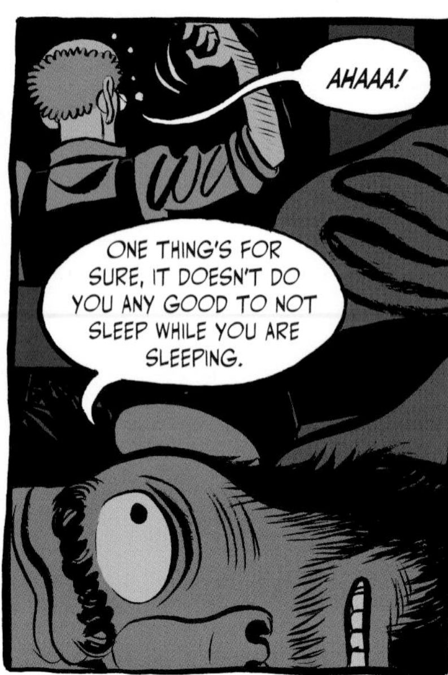
AHAAA!
ONE THING'S FOR SURE, IT DOESN'T DO YOU ANY GOOD TO NOT SLEEP WHILE YOU ARE SLEEPING.

IT'S BIG HERE.
NEVER SEEN THE BOUNDARIES.

IT'S NOT THAT MUCH FUN, IN ANY CASE.

YOU DON'T REMEMBER WHERE YOU ESCAPED FROM?
UP.
YEAH, THAT'S FOR SURE.

SIGH.

YOUR FATHER...
VERY DIFFERENT MACHINE FROM YOU.

YOU MEAN THAT WE'RE NOT ALIKE?
NOT THE SAME.

NO?
BUT WE HAVE THE SAME ELBOWS.
THE WAY I BEND MY ARM, SEE? MY DAD'S IS THE SAME.
HIS BENDS THE EXACT SAME WAY, LIKE THIS, SEE?

IT'S NORMAL, HE'S MY DADDY.
ISN'T THAT FUNNY?

FUNNY, YOU KNOW?
DON'T YOU LAUGH DOWN HERE?

YOU KNOW... LIKE A GOOD LAUGH.
HA HA HA!
LIKE THIS?

?
AAH!

HELP!
ADDIDAS
WAIT!

IT'S JIM.
MCMULLAN'S SON.
?

THE MCMULLANS ARE THE BASTARDS WHO STEAL DAD'S CONTRACTS!

HA HA. HE MUST BE SCARED.
COME ON, WE'LL GO GET HIM. MAYBE HE REMEMBERS THE WAY OUT!
NO, NO, VERY DANGEROUS.

COME ON!
YOUR FRIENDS WILL BE SHOCKED TO SEE SO MANY HUMANS AMONG THEM!

CLIC

THE BIG ONE, VERY DANGE-ROUS. VERY STRONG.
NOT STAY HERE.

WHAT ARE THEY GOING TO DO WITH HIM?
DON'T KNOW. NEVER SEE THIS!

WE HAVE TO CREATE A DISTRACTION!

?
A DISTRAC-TION!
I SAW A KIND OF WESTERN ON TV. THERE WAS A GIRL, A SORT OF SCHOOLTEACHER. VERY PRETTY WITH LONG, BLOND HAIR...
SO PRETTY THAT EVEN THE ADULTS ENDED UP GOING TO SCHOOL. I KNOW, BECAUSE ONE OF THEM, A COWBOY, SAID THAT HE WANTED TO BE HER STUDENT.
SPENCER SOMETHING...

ANYWAY.
THE INDIANS CAPTURED HER AND TIED HER TO A TREE AND DANCED AROUND HER LIKE THEY DO.
SPENCER-WHATEVER WAS REALLY MAD. HE CLENCHED HIS JAW UNTIL IT ACHED.
HE GRABBED HIS FRIEND AND THEY RODE TO WHERE THE INDIANS WERE CAMPED AND DANCING AROUND THE TREE.
AND THEN HE SAID:

"WE HAVE TO CREATE A DISTRACTION."

SO?

DISTRACTION?
WHAT IS THAT?

I DON'T KNOW FOR SURE, BUT IN THE END THE SCHOOLTEACHER WAS ON THAT SPENCER GUY'S HORSE. HE WAS LOOKING STRAIGHT AHEAD AND LOOKING ALL PROUD LIKE HE ACCOMPLISHED SOMETHING EXTRAORDINARY.
IN THE INDIAN CAMP, THE INDIANS WERE RUNNING EVERYWHERE. THEY WERE IN A PANIC. THEY HAD NO ONE TO DANCE AROUND.
SPENCER SAID, "I MAY HAVE BEEN A BIT LATE, BUT THE INDIANS ARE PATIENT."
OR SOMETHING LIKE THAT, I DIDN'T QUITE UNDERSTAND.
AND HE SMILED.

SHE SAID, "YOU ARE MAGNIFICENT, SPENCER-WHATEVER."
CRAZY!

NO, NO, IT'S A WESTERN, IT'S NORMAL.
AAAAH

HELP!

OKAY, FORGET THE DISTRACTION.
I'LL RUN ALL OVER THE PLACE AND YOU GRAB JIM.
CLIC
AAAAAH
WE'LL MEET BACK HERE.

DON'T...
AAA AAA...

AAAA...

PLAF

AAAA...

AAAA...

?

AAAA...

WHAT ARE YOU DOING HERE? YOU SHOULDN'T BE HERE!
WHAT DO YOU MEAN I SHOULDN'T BE HERE?
I CAME TO GET YOU!

LITTLE BOYS SHOULDN'T BE DOWN HERE.
AND WHAT SHOULD LITTLE BOYS DO THEN?

NORMAL STUFF. PLAY WITH THEIR DOG, ACT LIKE IDIOTS, GET NOSEBLEEDS.
NORMAL STUFF.

AND WHAT ABOUT YOU?
SAME FOR ME.

WHAT DO YOU MEAN SAME FOR YOU?
FORGET IT.

WHO'S THIS GUY?
A FRIEND. HE WAS TAKING CARE OF MY MACHINE!

WHAT MACHINE?
WHAT THE HELL IS DOWN THERE?

IT'S THE MACHINE WORLD. ONE HUMAN, ONE MACHINE. WE COULD HAVE GONE TO SEE YOURS HAD WE HAD THE TIME, BUT WE'RE GOING BACK UP 'CAUSE I FEEL BAD THAT I'VE BEEN HAVING FUN DOWN HERE WHILE MY DADDY IS UP THERE ALL ALONE.
WHAT KIND OF ANIMAL ARE THESE THINGS?
THEY'RE NOT ANIMALS!
THEY'RE SOMETHING ELSE!

THIS IS NONSENSE!
WELL, IT'S OUR NONSENSE NOW.

ANYWAY, THAT WAS AN AWESOME DISTRACTION BACK THERE.
OH, YEAH? YOU SAW THAT MOVIE TOO?

WHAT MOVIE?
THE WESTERN.

tip tip tip
tip tip tip
tap tap
tap tap
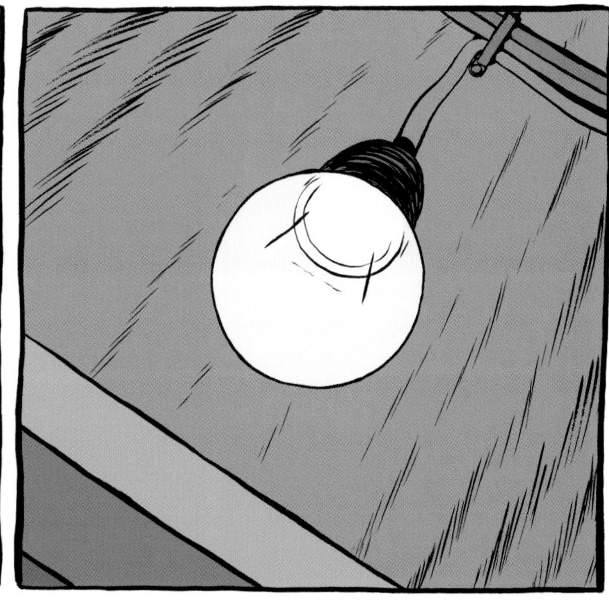

Paf!
AAAA

FOR CHRIST'S SAKE.
THERE'S A RUNG MISSING!

TUNNEL C!
EVANS, ARTUR, MULLER, FLANHAGGAN...

WE'RE GETTING OUT OF HERE.
TODAY.

I'M FED UP, JULIUS.
I'M SORRY.

YOU'RE AN IDIOT!
I'M GETTING OUT ALONE THEN, JUST WAIT, WAIT AND SEE.

YEAH, I'LL PROBABLY SEE YOU LOCKED UP!

TUNNEL B: SINUS, BULL...
EME.

GO AHEAD.
DUMP THE BAGS.

FOR THE LOVE OF GOD.

WE DON'T EVEN KNOW WHERE THESE CARTS GO!
COUGH!
YOU DIG A HOLE, YOU GOTTA TAKE THE DIRT OUT, OTHERWISE THERE'S NO HOLE.
COUGH! COUGH!

YEAH.
YEAH.
DUMP MY BAG.

YOU'RE GOING TO SUFFOCATE!

TA-DAH!

DUMP MOY BWAG!
WELL, YOU'RE NOT STUPID; I'LL GIVE YOU THAT.

tap tap

CLUNK

IF YOU WANT TO FIND THE EXIT, IT'S SIMPLE: HAVE SOMEONE CHASE YOU!
YEAH, WELL, I FOUND YOU, THAT'S GOOD ENOUGH. I'M GETTING OUT OF HERE!

HOW DO YOU KNOW THAT'S THE RIGHT LADDER?

I DON'T CARE AS LONG AS IT'S GOING UP!

OKAY.

CRRUNCH
CRRAK

BROMBROLOBOM

WELL, THAT SHOULD CREATE SOME WORK FOR MY DAD!
THIS CHIMNEY IS MINE!
MIGHT I REMIND YOU THAT YOU AND YOUR FATHER HAVE STOLEN ENOUGH CONTRACTS FROM US!

YEAH, MAYBE.
IT'S 'CAUSE HE'S SHORT ON CASH!
AND YOU THINK WE'RE NOT?

WELCOME TO THE CITY!

WE'RE NOT FAR FROM JIM'S PAWNSHOP.

THEY'RE NOT ANIMALS? YIKES!
WHAT ARE YOU GOING TO DO WITH HIM; PEOPLE ARE BOUND TO SEE HIM!

WE'LL FIND DAD IN THAT PIT AND THEN WE'LL SEE.
I'LL HIDE HIM SOMEWHERE.

YEAH, WELL, IT'S NOT LIKE HE'S A HAMSTER.
WE DON'T EVEN KNOW WHAT HE EATS.
IF HE EATS SEEDS OR I DON'T KNOW WHAT!

WHAT'S THIS "PIT"?

I DON'T KNOW.
I HAVE TO GO AND ASK AT THE POLICE DEPARTMENT.

WITH HIM?

I'M OUTTA HERE!

I'M GOING TO FIND MY DAD WHO'S PROBABLY WORRIED THAT I NEVER CAME BACK UP!
GOOD LUCK WITH ALL THAT. I JUST HOPE I SEE YOU LATER RA-THER THAN SOONER!

OKAY, IT'S MY TURN TO HIDE YOU.
THERE ARE BAD PEOPLE HERE, TOO.

FLIC
FLOC
FLOC
FLIC
FLOC
FLIC
FLIC
FLOC
FLIC

POLICE

STAY HERE FOR A SECOND.
I'LL COME GET YOU IF THEY DON'T COOPERATE.

WE'LL CREATE A DISTRACTION!

EXCUSE ME!
?

EXCUSE ME!

WHERE IS THE BIG PIT?

YOU!
GET THIS KID OUT OF HERE!

WHOA, WHOA, DON'T DO ANYTHING CRAZY! I HAVE A BIG MONSTER WITH ME. AND AFTER SEEING HOW HE DESTROYED A CHIMNEY I CAN ASSURE YOU HE'LL MAKE MINCEMEAT OUT OF THIS POLICE DEPARTMENT!

HMMM... A BIG MONSTER?
YUP.

SO, WHERE'S THIS PIT?
I HAVE TO GO GET MY FATHER. YOU PUT HIM IN THERE BY MISTAKE!
MY FATHER NEVER HURT ANYONE, HE'S A CHIMNEY SWEEP!

OH, YES, I REMEMBER.
THE ONE I SMOKED OUT.
HA HA HA

HMMM.
AND YOU ARE THE LITTLE GIRL STUCK IN THE CHIMNEY.
YES! THAT'S IT. THAT'S EXACTLY IT!
YOU'RE ONE HECK OF A COMMISSIONER!

SO, THIS PIT?
YOUR MONSTER ...
YES?

ARE HIS NAILS CLEAN?

I DON'T THINK SO. NO, NOT WHERE HE'S FROM.
OKAY! INTO THE PIT THEN!
HA HA HA HA HA.. HA..

HA HA HA!
WHATEVER.

OKAY THEN. LADIES AND GENTLEMEN, THERE IS GOING TO BE A BIT OF A COMMOTION. THOSE WHO WISH TO LEAVE MAY DO SO IMMEDIATELY.

AHEM. SO, AS I WAS SAYING, IN A MOMENT A BIG MONSTER IS GOING TO COME DOWN THOSE STAIRS.
HE'LL BREAK EVERYTHING, ESPECIALLY YOU, AND THEN HE'LL SMASH YOUR HEAD WITH THE TYPEWRITER.
I DON'T REALLY KNOW HIS NAME. BUT, IN ANY CASE, HE'S NOT BAD.

WILL YOU GET THE HELL OUT OF HERE!

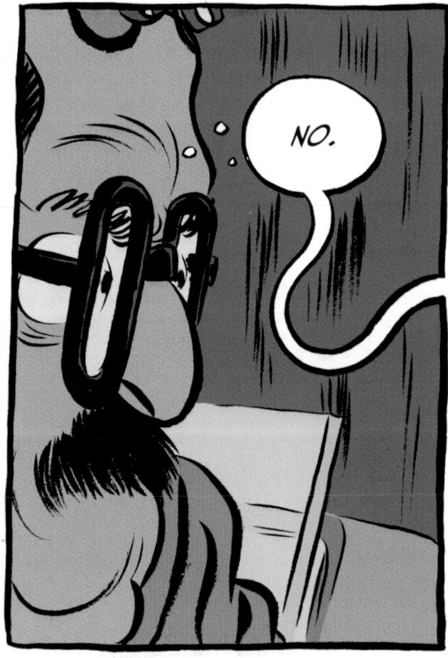
NO.

AAAAAA
AAAAAAAAA

AAAA
AA
AAA
A
AA
AA

AAAAAA
AAAAAAH

WELL, DO SOMETHING, FOR CHRIST'S SAKE.
SHOOT HIM!
AAAA

NO.
I...
...
I'M NOT TOO SURE ...

YEAH.
YOU PROBABLY SHOULDN'T!

PANT PANT

CRRUNCH

WOW, YOU DON'T SEE THAT EVERY DAY, DE-MOLISHED!

I'M GOING...
TO GET...
UM, SOMETHING.

BAD?

MORE LIKE STUPID, REALLY.
STUPID?

YEAH, STUPID. STUPID IS WHEN SOMEONE IS SLOW TO UNDERSTAND SOMETHING OR DOESN'T WANT TO UNDERSTAND OR CAN'T, OR WHO THINKS THEY UNDERSTAND BUT IN REALITY DOESN'T UNDERSTAND ANYTHING AT ALL.

I UNDERSTAND.

YEAH, OF COURSE YOU DO, YOU'RE MY FRIEND!

UH!

TUNK
PLAF!
OUCH!

GLUNK
?

0 15:
SSSSSSSSSSSSSSSSSSSSS

AAAA

POUF
POUF

ADDIDAS!

35 0 0 12

I WARN YOU.
IT'S OKAY.

AFTER YOUR FATHER...
FIX MACHINE!

THE PIT?

TOWARDS THE INDUSTRIAL CITY, AFTER THE BRIDGE,
THERE ARE TONS OF TRUCKS, YOU CAN'T MISS IT.

WHAT...
WHAT IS THAT HUGE THING?

I TOLD YOU...
HE'S MY FRIEND.

tAC tAC

BAKER 321
PUF
PUF
STALAG17

HOP
HOP
HOP

?

WHAT THE HELL ARE YOU DOING HERE?
WHERE IS ADDIDAS?

MISTER EME?
ALREADY?
WHAT DO YOU MEAN "ALREADY"?
WHERE IS ADDIDAS?

WELL, SHE SAID SHE WAS GOING TO GET YOU FROM THE BIG PIT.
I WAS WAITING FOR YOU BECAUSE I CAN'T FIND MY FATHER...

THIS ISN'T HAPPENING!

I JUST GOT *OUT* OF THE PIT.
I GOT OUT!
AH, WELL, ADDIDAS DIDN'T KNOW.
SHE WENT THERE WITH THE MONSTER.

THE WHAT?

YEAH, IT'S HARD TO BELIEVE, BUT I SAW IT, I SWEAR. AND THERE ARE MORE LIKE HIM EVEN, DOWN THERE!
DOWN THERE?

YEAH, DOWN THERE, ALL THE WAY DOWN.
THAT WAS WHERE ADDIDAS WAS!
ARE THERE PHONES DOWN THERE?
WHAT?

NO...
NOTHING.

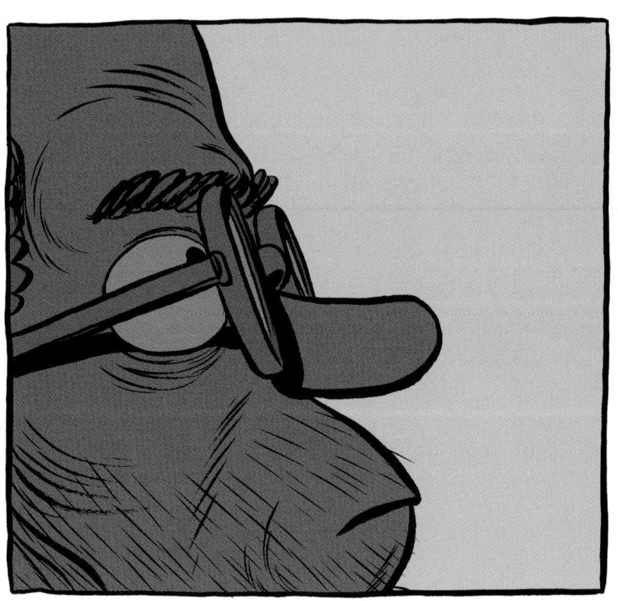

COME ON!

SAY, MISTER EME, YOU'RE IN PRETTY GOOD SHAPE!

WE'LL GET THEM ALL. ADDIDAS, HER MONSTER, AND YOUR FATHER!
MY FATHER IS THERE TOO?

CRRAK!
AAAAA
HELP!

AAAAAA
AAAAAA
AAAA

BAAAA
AAAA
HELP!
AAAAA

OBVIOUSLY IF YOU ACT LIKE THAT THIS IS GOING TO BE EASY.
NO NEED TO CREATE DISTRACTIONS.

AAAA
AAAA

DAD!

DAAAD!

ADDIDAS!

WAIT...
IT'S MCMULLAN.

YOUR FATHER GOT OUT!
HE ESCAPED?

JESUS.
YES.
I THINK SO.

SIGH.

WHAT IS THAT THING?

A MONSTER, YOU SAY?
VERY BIG AND...
AND STRONG AND STUFF.

DAD!

ADDIDAS!
DAD!

12.04. FREDERIK — WAZEM

A BIG, BLACK MONSTER WITH YELLOW EYES, HUGE ARMS, AND HUGE HANDS. HE SQUASHED THE TELEPHONE WITH ONE FINGER!
AND THE WAY HE LOOKED AT ME...
IT WAS LIKE...A MEDICAL EXAMINATION!

SNIFF...

I TRIED TO HOLD THEM OFF... TO...
"THEM"?!

YES, HE WAS WITH A GIRL.
A LITTLE GIRL.

SHE SAID HE WAS HER FRIEND! CAN YOU BELIEVE THAT?! AS IF HE WAS HER PET, HER TEDDY BEAR OR SOMETHING! "COME HERE. SIT! DON'T DO NUMBER TWO! SQUASH THAT PHONE..."
SO, A LITTLE GIRL AND HER MONSTER CAME IN HERE AND PRACTICALLY DESTROYED YOUR HEADQUARTERS?

EXACTLY!
AND THAT'S WHAT I SHOULD WRITE IN THE REPORT?
WRITE WHAT YOU WANT IN YOUR REPORT! I DON'T CARE! I TOLD YOU EXACTLY WHAT HAPPENED!

I DON'T THINK I CAN WRITE THAT IN THE REPORT...
WHAT?
YOU DON'T BELIEVE ME?
YOU IDIOT, WHY WOULD I EVEN MAKE THAT UP? I AM A COMMISSIONER! I AM NOT A...A CHILD!

I DON'T EVEN HAVE IMAGINATION... I DON'T LIVE IN A FANTASY WORLD...
I AM A COMMISSIONER... I SEE WHAT I SEE AND WHAT I SAW WAS REAL AND I DON'T SEE ANY OTHER...

IN ANY CASE, I WASN'T THE ONLY WITNESS! MY MEN WERE THERE, AND SO WAS A WHOLE CROWD OF PEOPLE!

HMM... NO.
NO ONE SAW ANYTHING.

WHAT?! WHAT, "NO ONE SAW ANYTHING"?!
THERE WERE AT LEAST FIFTY PEOPLE AT HEADQUARTERS!

ENOUGH.

WAIT! WAIT! I... THIS IS A SET-UP! THERE IS A...THERE'S A MONSTER RUNNING AROUND TOWN!

NOOOOO!

IT WAS THEM...
IT'S WHAT WE THOUGHT.

I DON'T UNDERSTAND HOW THE TWO OF THEM MET. THERE ARE NO CHILDREN IN THE PIT. THEY COULDN'T HAVE MET THERE! ARE THERE ANY OTHER PITS THAT WE DON'T KNOW ABOUT?

THAT'S IMPOSSIBLE!
WE DON'T HAVE MUCH TIME. WE MUST BE FIRST TO GET OUR HANDS ON THOSE MACHINES.
WE'LL PUT HALF THE TOWN INTO THE PIT AND HALF OUR GUYS ON FINDING THAT GIRL AND HER MONSTER.

AT THE SAME TIME...
...THEY CAN'T REALLY GO UNNOTICED, CAN THEY!

THAT IS QUITE AN INCREDIBLE STORY, ADDIDAS!

ISN'T IT?
THEY'RE NOT STORIES! I SAW ALL OF IT! IT'S ALL TRUE! THERE'S A SCREWY WORLD DOWN THERE!

WE HAVE TO PLUG THAT MACHINE BACK IN! I'M COUNTING ON YOU, MISTER! WE'RE TALKING ABOUT MY DAUGHTER'S LIFE HERE!
?

OKAY! WHERE IS IT? HOW DO WE GET THERE?
ITCH...

UH... DAD?
WHAT?

THE COUNTRYSIDE, DAD!

MY MACHINE'S IN THE DEAD MACHINE DEPOT AND I'M NOT DEAD, SEE?! DON'T YOU SEE!
TAP
TAP
TAP

SO LET'S LEAVE THE MACHINE WHERE IT IS AND ESCAPE TO THE COUNTRYSIDE! WE'LL HIDE LIKE FUGITIVES!
BUT WE DON'T EVEN KNOW WHAT'S WAITING FOR US IN THE DAMN COUNTRYSIDE, ADDIDAS, OR EVEN WHERE IT IS!
EXACTLY! IT'S THE PERFECT HIDING SPOT!

SIGH

IT WOULD BE GOOD IF EACH COUNTRYSIDE HAD A DIRECT ROUTE! SIMPLE AND DIRECT... LIFE WOULD BE GOOD WHEREVER WE WENT AND THERE WOULDN'T BE ANY MORE SUFFERING!... SOMEONE ABLE TO TAKE US BY THE HAND AND FIND THE ROAD...TO IMAGINE IT. INVENT IT AND PUT US ON THE RIGHT PATH.
THAT WOULD REALLY BE WONDERFUL.

I'M SORRY, ADDIDAS, I'M NOT AS STRONG AS I USED TO BE... I USED TO FEEL THAT I HAD A ROCK IN MY FIST, A REAL BIG MEAN ONE, BUT NOW IT'S CRUMBLED INTO SAND. AND THAT SAND HAS SIFTED THROUGH MY FINGERS...
AND NOW THE SAND JUST KEEPS ON DISAPPEA-RING EVEN THOUGH IT'S NOT EVEN SLIPPING THROUGH MY FINGERS ANYMORE!

I DON'T EVEN KNOW IF IT HAPPENED ALL AT ONCE OR IF IT CREPT UP ON ME.
I THINK TODAY IS A GOOD DAY TO PICK UP A NEW ROCK, DAD.
HMPH.

WHAT IF WE WENT BACK DOWN?
...BY THE CHIMNEY NEAR JIM'S PAWNSHOP?
THE CHIMNEY THAT GOT DESTROYED WHEN WE CAME OUT?

HEY, WHAT ARE YOU TALKING ABOUT? THIS HAS NOTHING TO DO WITH US! I'M NOT GOING ANYWHERE AND ESPECIALLY NOT DOWN THERE! AND YOU HAVE NO BUSINESS IN THIS CRAP!
MY GOD, IF SOMETHING HAPPENED TO YOU... I... I WOULD BEAT THE LIVING DAYLIGHTS OUT OF YOU!
YOU PREFER TO GO BACK TO THE PIT, DAD?

LISTEN YOU...
GULP.

WE'RE ALL IN THE SAME BOAT, AREN'T WE?
WE'RE TALKING ABOUT MY DAUGHTER'S LIFE HERE!

AND YOUR KID MAKES SENSE. THERE ARE PROBABLY THREE HUNDRED COPS ON OUR TAIL BY NOW.

AND ON TOP OF THAT, ADDIDAS COULD HAVE AN EPISODE AT ANY SECOND! IT'S INCREDIBLE SHE HASN'T YET.
CROÏNK

ARGH! DAMN THING!

KULUNK
KLUNK
CROÏNK
CROÏNK

KLUNK
KLUNK
KUNK

HOLY CRAP!

OH, YEAH! I FORGOT TO TELL YOU!
WHAT?!
WE TWEAKED YOUR MACHINE A BIT! YOU SHOULD BE A BIT STRONGER THAN NORMAL. LIKE A... SUPERHERO, KIND OF!

JESUS... THERE'S A LOT THOSE MACHINES CAN DO.

WE SHOULD MAKE MY DAD LIKE YOURS, NO?
WE SHOULDN'T MEDDLE WITH THE BALANCE IN THE MECHANICS.
APPARENTLY IT'S FRAGILE... THEN WE'LL HAVE TO PUT IT ALL BACK THE SAME WAY.

OKAY, IT'S NOT OVER YET! LET'S GO! I'M GOING TO FIND THE COUNTRYSIDE FOR YOU! THE ROAD AND THE WHOLE SHEBANG IF THAT'S WHAT YOU WANT!

AFTER ALL, THERE IS LESS RISK DOWN THERE THAN UP HERE WITH THE BIG...BIG GUY THERE! SOMEONE MIGHT SEE US!
LET'S GO TO JIM'S PAWNSHOP AND INTO THE OTHER WORLD. HA HA HA!

THEY'RE HERE.
YES...
YES... THEY'RE HIDING UNDER THE TRAIN STATION.

THERE ARE OTHER PEOPLE WITH THE GIRL AND THE BEAST.
NO, NO...
DEFINITELY NOT A THREAT!
A COUPLE OF GUYS WITH KIDS.

UM...
YES...WITH THE BEAST, IN ANY CASE.

DON'T TOUCH THE GIRL AND THE BEAST?
BUT, UM, ISN'T THAT THE ANIMAL THAT DESTROYED THE POLICE HQ? ...OKAY.
ASH
OKAY...
WE WON'T LOSE THEM.

eureta

GOD DAMN IT, THIS ISN'T HAPPENING! THIS IS NOT HAPPENING!

SIGH.

REMEMBER ME, *COMMISSIONER*?

OKAY, LET'S CALM DOWN, JUST CALM DOWN... WE'RE ALL IN THE SAME BOAT HERE, NO? NO FUNNY STUFF, OKAY?
YES, BUT BEFORE...BEFORE THE SAME BOAT... DO YOU REMEMBER ***WHY*** YOU THREW ME IN HERE?

ORDERS.
I HAD TO SEND AS MANY PEOPLE HERE AS POSSIBLE.

ORDERS FROM THOSE GOVERNMENT BASTARDS!
THE REASONS DIDN'T MATTER! HAD TO SEND PEOPLE TO DIG!

HEY!
I TOLD YOU, IT WASN'T ME!

BREAK IT UP AND GET BACK TO DIGGING!
WHAT DO YOU THINK THIS IS, TEA TIME?

I AM GOING TO GO CRAZY IF I DON'T GET OUT OF HERE.
THESE REDNECKS ARE GOING TO RIP ME APART AND LEAVE MY BODY TO ROT.
THE SAME THAT WILL HAPPEN TO THAT MONSTER AND HIS LITTLE GIRL, IF YOU WANT MY OPINION!

YEAH, HEADED FOR THE TALL CHIMNEYS...
NO, WE WON'T LOSE THEM...
THAT'S IT.

TUK-TUK

CHLAK

NOOO!

TAC
TAC
TAC
TAC

SEND THE GIRL FORWARD!

WHAT?
WHY THE GIRL?

COME ON, COME ON!

UM...
I MEAN...
NO...

NO?

WELL...
NO...
RIGHT?

NO?! WHAT DO YOU MEAN, "NO"?

I MEAN, I'M NOT SENDING HER FORWARD.
NO ONE IS GOING ANYWHERE! YOU'RE GOING TO BACK AWAY AND LET US GO!
YOU DON'T UNDERSTAND WHAT'S GOING ON HERE.

YES, I UNDERSTAND PERFECTLY! IT'S TIME FOR ME TO PICK UP A ROCK AND HOLD IT TIGHTLY IN MY FISTS AND NOT LET IT TURN INTO SAND SO THAT IT SIFTS THROUGH MY FINGERS. THAT'S THE SITUATION! IT'S PERFECTLY CLEAR TO ME. BUT I DOUBT THAT YOU, THAT YOU CAN UNDERSTAND IT!

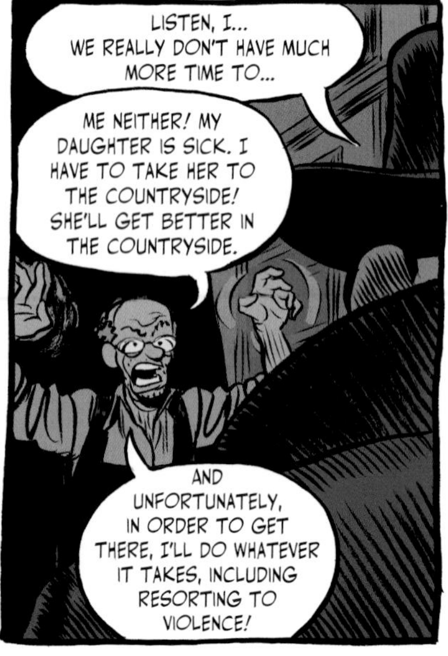
LISTEN, I... WE REALLY DON'T HAVE MUCH MORE TIME TO...
ME NEITHER! MY DAUGHTER IS SICK. I HAVE TO TAKE HER TO THE COUNTRYSIDE! SHE'LL GET BETTER IN THE COUNTRYSIDE.
AND UNFORTUNATELY, IN ORDER TO GET THERE, I'LL DO WHATEVER IT TAKES, INCLUDING RESORTING TO VIOLENCE!

HE'S CRAZY.

DON'T BE AN IDIOT. THINK OF YOUR DAUGHTER. IT WOULD BE STUPID TO...

PLAF!

ADDIDAS!

WHAT THE HELL IS THIS NOW?

CLAC
CLAC
WAIT!

AAAAAAAA!

RAAAAAA!
CRRAAK

CRASH
HUMPH

SPLAF

BLAM!
BLAM!

CLAC
Pioooouuu
Pioouuu

BLAM
STOP! WATCH THE GIRL, FOR GOD'S SAKE!

RAAAAAA!

COUGH...
COUGH...

GRAB THE KIDS!
OKAY.

?!?

HAP!

AAAA!
?!

PAW!

DON'T SHOOT, FOR GOD'S SAKE!

AH!

DID YOU SEE THAT OLD GUY? UNBELIEVABLE! THEY HAD ACCESS TO THE MACHINES! WE'VE BEEN DOUBLE-CROSSED! DAMN KID! UNBELIEVABLE!
DID YOU SEE HIM? INCREDIBLE!

THEY DISAPPEARED DOWN THE OTHER SIDE!

SHIT!

YOU AND I WILL CHAT...
ONE WAY OR ANOTHER.

BOSS, WE FOUND THIS UNDER ONE OF THE CARS AT THE TRAIN STATION.

HM.

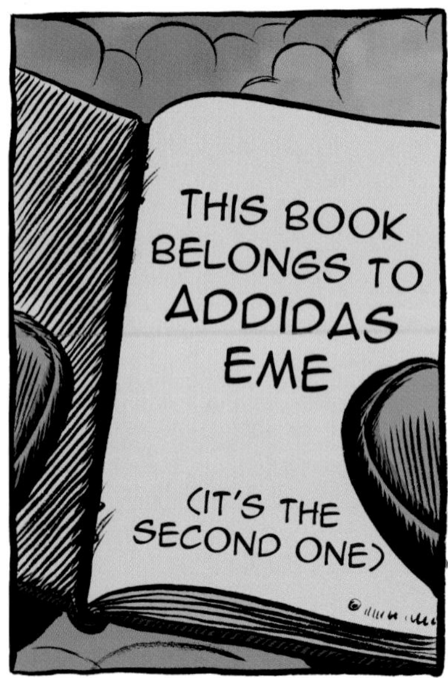
THIS BOOK BELONGS TO ADDIDAS EME
(IT'S THE SECOND ONE)

IT'S HERS, "ADDIDAS EME." AND THE GUY WHOSE STRENGTH INCREASED TENFOLD IS HER FATHER, "JULIUS EME," HE'S THE ONE WHO ESCAPED FROM THE PIT.

WE'LL ID THE OTHER TWO LATER. IT'S POSSIBLE THAT THE OTHER MAN WAS THE SECOND ESCAPEE FROM THE PIT.
403-250
EME

WE SHOULD REALLY GET YOU THE SAME POWERS AS MR. EME. DID YOU SEE THAT CRAZ--
YEAH, OKAY, ENOUGH ALREADY!
WHAT WOULD BE GOOD IS IF WE GOT OUT OF THIS MESS WITHOUT TOO MUCH DAMAGE.

ANYWAY...
ALL THIS...
YOU REALLY GOTTA SEE IT TO BELIEVE IT.

I'M OKAY.
YOU KNOW, DOWN HERE, I NEVER PASS OUT!

WHERE'S MY FRIEND?
AH... UM...
HE...HE STAYED UP THERE.

BUT...
THEY'RE GOING TO HURT HIM!
WE CAN'T LEAVE HIM. HE DOESN'T KNOW ANYTHING ABOUT OUR WORLD.

HE'S PRETTY STRONG, HE'LL BE FINE.
WE CAN'T GO BACK UP THERE, ADDIDAS.

(SIGH)
IS THERE ANY WAY THAT HUMANKIND CAN STOP HURTING OTHERS, EVEN INADVERTENTLY?

I'M TIRED.
DID YOU SEE HOW IMPORTANT ADDIDAS WAS TO THEM?
THEY IGNORED US COMPLETELY. THEY WANTED ADDIDAS AND NO ONE ELSE.

I WONDER WHAT YOU COULD HAVE DONE TO THEM.
THEY WANT TO CONTROL THE MACHINES.

OH BOY... I'M BEGINNING TO UNDERSTAND!
THIS IS SERIOUS!
IT'S SERIOUS FOR YOU, NOT FOR ME. I'M WORRIED ABOUT YOU!
WHAT DO YOU MEAN, FOR US?
MY MACHINE CAN'T BE CONTROLLED. IT'S UNPLUGGED.

IT'S FUNNY...
FUNNY?

YES, I THINK IT HAPPENED WHEN I SAID I NO LONGER WANTED TO BE UP THERE. UP THERE, EVERYONE CAN SEE YOU, THAT'S HOW IT IS. THE WHOLE WORLD CAN SEE YOU, EVEN THE BAD GUYS. I DIDN'T WANT THAT ANYMORE. I WANTED TO BE IN A PLACE WHERE NO ONE COULD SEE US. I THOUGHT HERE... BUT EVEN HERE...

OKAY, LET'S GO TO THE COUNTRYSIDE THEN!
WE'RE SURE TO GET SOMEWHERE IF WE WALK IN ONE DIRECTION LONG ENOUGH.

WE CAN INVENT SOME AMAZING STORIES, IN FACT.
AND WE CAN BELIEVE THEM FOR A WHILE. NO MATTER HOW CRAZY OR UNBELIEVABLE THEY ARE!
WE JUST HAVE TO BELIEVE IN THEM, THAT'S ALL.
WE CAN EVEN BE HAPPY THAT WAY.
THEY'RE NOT LIES. THEY'RE EVEN MORE REAL THAN REALITY.

COUGH, COUGH.
BUT RIGHT NOW, I CAN'T BELIEVE THEM...
I'M TOO TIRED.

ADDIDAS, YOU CAN'T GIVE UP.
IT'S TOO LATE TO GIVE UP!

HEY, IT'S STARTING TO GET COLD!
KEEP GOING!

WHAT THE HELL IS THAT?!

ARE WE GOING TO DIE?
OF COURSE NOT! DON'T THINK LIKE THAT! WHY WOULD WE DIE?

WOULD YOU HAVE ANY REGRETS IF YOU DIED NOW?
HMM.

I CHEATED AT CARDS ONCE OR TWICE!
THAT'S IT?

AND I COULDN'T SAVE YOUR MOTHER, BUT I SWEAR I WON'T LET THAT HAPPEN TO YOU.
IT MAY BE OUT OF YOUR CONTROL...
WHAT ARE YOU SAYING? YOU'RE A CHILD, YOU DEPEND ON ME!

ANYWAY, THEY ARE MY REGRETS; THEY HAVE NOTHING TO DO WITH YOU.
YOUR REGRETS ARE THE ONES THAT CONTROL YOU.

WE HAVE TO FIND SHELTER!
NO KIDDING.

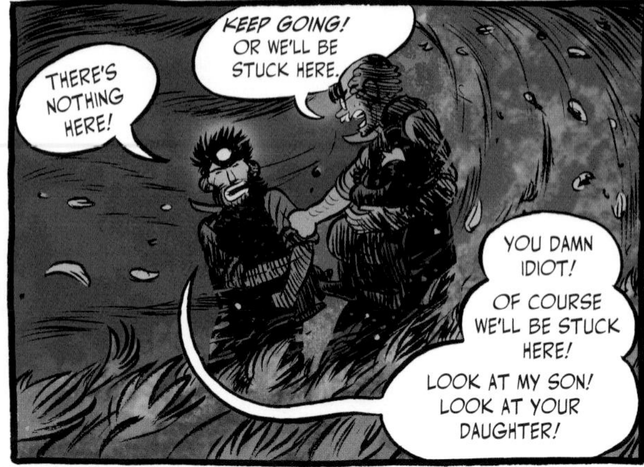

THERE'S NOTHING HERE!
KEEP GOING! OR WE'LL BE STUCK HERE.
YOU DAMN IDIOT!
OF COURSE WE'LL BE STUCK HERE!
LOOK AT MY SON! LOOK AT YOUR DAUGHTER!

I THINK WE'VE ARRIVED.
WHAT?!

BONK!

THERE'S A...
YES, YES.
CLIMB!

WOULD YOU LOOK AT THAT!
WHAT DO YOU SEE?
NOTHING!

WHAT, "NOTHING"?!
WELL... NOTHING! I DON'T SEE ANYTHING!

ODD... MAYBE THIS IS THE COUNTRYSIDE.
THIS IS NOT HOW I IMAGINED IT.
HM...
I DON'T THINK THIS IS THE COUNTRY-SIDE.
?

HOW DO YOU KNOW IF YOU'VE NEVER EVEN SEEN IT?
HEY. IT'S NICE HERE.
BRR BRR.

I THOUGHT THERE WOULD BE HILLS, SWAMPS, RIVERS, FIELDS, GULLIES, FORESTS, GLADES...
STUFF LIKE THAT ...

YEAH, WELL, WE DON'T EVEN KNOW WHAT ALL THAT LOOKS LIKE. SO MAYBE WE'RE IN THE HILLS AND STUFF.
DON'T BE STUPID!
WE CAN'T SEE ANYTHING!

AH!
THERE'S A HOUSE OVER THERE, THOUGH.

A HOUSE?

5

SAY, WHAT IS BACK THERE? BECAUSE IT'S MOVING QUITE A BIT, AND...

UM.

I DON'T HAVE MUCH TIME, SO LET'S MAKE THIS SIMPLE AND STRAIGHTFORWARD...
...AS MUCH AS POSSIBLE.

YOU EXIST. YOU'RE A PRISONER.
THOSE ARE FACTS.
YOU MET THE LITTLE GIRL, ADDIDAS. THAT'S ANOTHER FACT.
I WANT TO KNOW WHERE AND WHEN AND WHY THAT GIRL?...

...I WANT TO KNOW WHAT THESE LINES IN HER BOOK MEAN.

AND, OF COURSE...
...I WANT TO KNOW WHERE I CAN FIND THE MACHINES.

HE SPEAKS?
HE SPEAKS...
BEFORE DESTROYING THE POLICE HQ, HE SAID, "NO."

NO?

NO.

OKAY!
YES, BUT FIRST WE NEED TO KNOW IF HE CAN BE HURT. AND HOW FAR WE CAN GO BEFORE WE KILL HIM.

WE HAVE NO IDEA WHAT HE'S MADE OF.
SHOULD WE EXAMINE HIM?
YES. EXAMINE HIM FIRST.

CLICK CLICK CLICK...

BEEP.

WELL! TO BE HONEST, I...

I HAVE NEVER SEEN ANYTHING LIKE THIS!
WHERE DID YOU FIND THIS...

SO... AND?

SO... UM...
HE'S A LITTLE LIKE US.
HE HAS A BIT OF EVERYTHING.
DO YOU TAKE ME FOR AN IDIOT?

WHAT DO YOU WANT TO DO WITH HIM? YOU KNOW, HE MUST BE A VERY RARE ANIMAL. I HAVE PERSONALLY NEVER SEEN ANYTHING LIKE IT ANYWHERE, AND--
YOU DON'T WANT TO KNOW.

I DON'T WANT TO KNOW?
NO. I'M SURE YOU PREFER NOT TO KNOW.
OKAY...
YES.

HIS NERVOUS SYSTEM IS IDENTICAL TO OURS: NERVES, CELLS, MUSCLES, ORGANS, BLOOD... HE'S STRONGER....
HE'S CROUCHING MOST OF THE TIME, AND HE MOSTLY USES HIS ARMS. BASICALLY, EVERYTHING IS...
LESS COMPLICA-TED.
LESS COM-PLICATED.
YES, HEARTIER... MORE...

HEY...
ADDIDAS EME'S BOOK!

?!?

YES.
OH?
SHE FREQUENTLY FALLS INTO A SORT OF COMA.
WITHOUT ANY MEDICAL REASON.
LOOK AT THIS BOOK. EACH TALLY MARK IS ONE OF HER FITS. SHE CAME TO SEE ME NOT LONG AGO... AN ODD CASE!

HMM.

I DID SOME RESEARCH. THERE ARE ONLY TWO OTHER SUCH CASES IN THE MEDICAL ARCHIVES. A LITTLE BOY AND A LITTLE GIRL.
QUITE THE CASE!

WHAT ARE THEIR NAMES?
"WERE" THEIR NAMES! THEY BOTH DISAPPEARED WHEN THEY WERE KIDS, EIGHTY AND NINETY-FIVE YEARS AGO, RESPECTIVELY.
SO THEY MUST BOTH BE DEAD BY NOW.

ONE WAS NAMED "SHELL EME" AND THE OTHER "WINSTON EME." IT HIT ME BECAUSE THEY ALL HAD THE SAME LAST NAME.
THEY ARE FROM THE SAME FAMILY?
ACTUALLY, NO. THEIR INDIVIDUAL NAMES DIDN'T FIT THE ADMINIS-TRATIVE FILES. ALL THREE FAMILIES WERE GIVEN THE SURNAME "EME" BY COINCIDENCE!

BUT, EXACTLY WHAT IS THIS BOOK DOING HERE?

YOU DON'T WANT TO KNOW.
I...
NO!

SIGH
CLINK

ARE YOU A SURGEON, DOCTOR?
NO.
NOT REALLY.
BUT YOU HAVE STUDIED MEDICINE, YOU MUST HAVE...
...PRACTICED ON CADAVERS.

YOU MUST HAVE ALSO DISSECTED FROGS, STUFF LIKE THAT. ISN'T THAT RIGHT, DOCTOR?
YOU HAVE SOME EXPERIENCE HANDLING A SCALPEL, DON'T YOU? YOU SEE, ABOVE ALL, I AM INTERESTED IN SKINNING AND CARVING.

I...I HAVE NEVER CARVED UP ANY...ANYONE...
WE HAVE RUN OUT OF TIME, DOCTOR.

I KNOW ONLY ONE SURE WAY TO MAKE SOMEONE TALK. SOME TOLD ME THEIR LIFE STORY FROM A TO Z. OTHERS WHO HAD NO IDEA WHAT I WANTED FROM THEM INVENTED STORIES THAT I COULD FILL TWENTY NOVELS WITH. IT'S HORRIBLE. EXTREMELY PAINFUL...UNIMAGINABLE SUFFERING. A SLOW DEATH.

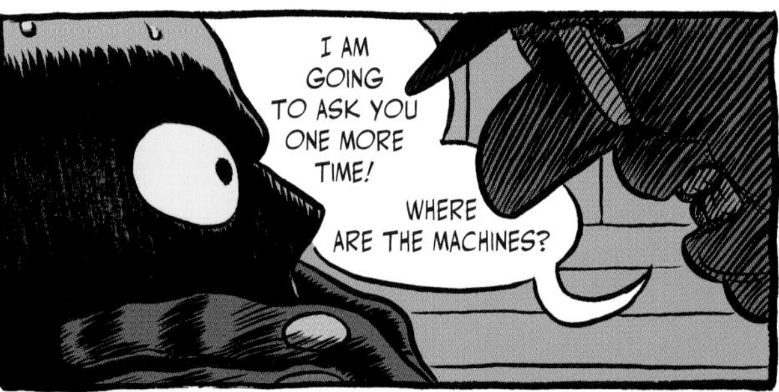
I AM GOING TO ASK YOU ONE MORE TIME!
WHERE ARE THE MACHINES?

FINE.
IT'S A SHAME.
I WOULD HAVE PREFERRED NOT TO WITNESS THIS EVER AGAIN.
I HAVE NO LIKING FOR THIS KIND OF THING.
WHAT ARE YOU GOING TO DO?

IT'S WHAT *YOU* ARE GOING TO DO!
I DON'T HAVE TIME TO CALL IN MY SPECIALIST.

YOU ARE GOING TO SKIN HIM ALIVE, DOCTOR!

MY SPECIALIST COULD SKIN A PERSON JUST LIKE HE WAS PEELING A PEACH. PERFECTION, IN ONE WHOLE PIECE. THE MOST IMPORTANT PART OF SKINNING IS TO DO IT SLOWLY. YOU CANNOT DAMAGE THE SKIN. YOU WILL DO IT AS PERFECTLY AS HE DID, DOCTOR.

YOU'RE INSANE! I REFUSE TO HAVE ANY PART IN THIS! FOR GOD'S SAKE, MAN, I'M A DOCTOR, NOT A...
YOU HAVE NO CHOICE.
AND IF YOU SCREW UP OR KILL HIM TOO QUICKLY, YOU WILL NEVER GET OUT OF HERE.
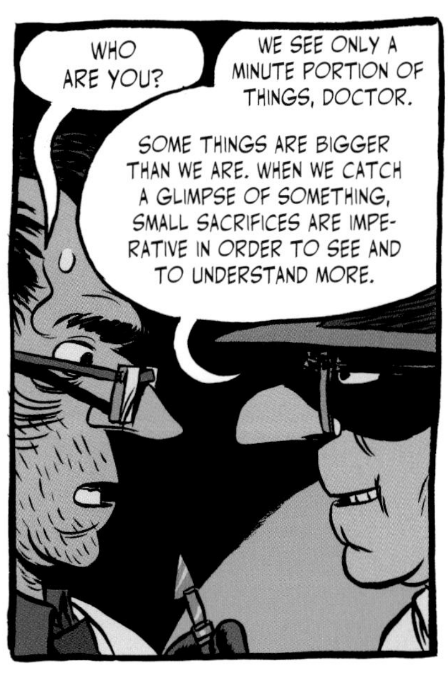
WHO ARE YOU?
WE SEE ONLY A MINUTE PORTION OF THINGS, DOCTOR.
SOME THINGS ARE BIGGER THAN WE ARE. WHEN WE CATCH A GLIMPSE OF SOMETHING, SMALL SACRIFICES ARE IMPERATIVE IN ORDER TO SEE AND TO UNDERSTAND MORE.

WITH THESE METHODS, I MANAGED TO OBTAIN THIS A COUPLE OF YEARS AGO...
TODAY, I WILL USE THE SAME METHODS TO GET EXPLANATIONS. IT'S ALL A MATTER OF LOGIC.

OKAY! LET'S DO IT!
MY SPECIALIST TIES THE HANDS AND FEET WITH STRAPS LAID OUT IN A SQUARE FASHION. AS A RESULT, THE VICTIM IS LAID IN THE SHAPE OF A CROSS, HORIZONTALLY.

HE BEGINS THE INCISION AT THE SHOULDER AND THEN SLICES TO THE WRISTS. YOU MUST TAKE CARE NOT TO MAKE THE INCISION TOO DEEPLY; OTHERWISE THE VICTIM WILL HEMORRHAGE AND, OBVIOUSLY, DIE TOO SOON.

WE CAN THEN MAKE OUT THE MUSCLES AND SOME VEINS. IT'S RATHER BEAUTIFUL. THE SKIN IS THEN REMOVED IN ONE WHOLE PIECE. IT MUST BE PAPER THIN. AT THIS STAGE, THE VICTIM'S SCREAMS ARE NO LONGER OF THIS WORLD.
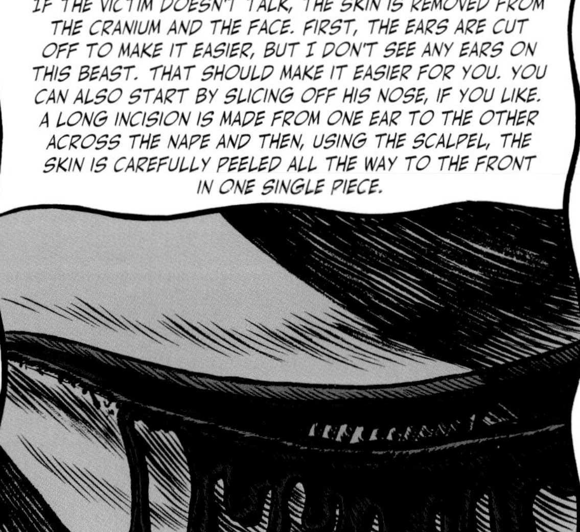
IF THE VICTIM DOESN'T TALK, THE SKIN IS REMOVED FROM THE CRANIUM AND THE FACE. FIRST, THE EARS ARE CUT OFF TO MAKE IT EASIER, BUT I DON'T SEE ANY EARS ON THIS BEAST. THAT SHOULD MAKE IT EASIER FOR YOU. YOU CAN ALSO START BY SLICING OFF HIS NOSE, IF YOU LIKE. A LONG INCISION IS MADE FROM ONE EAR TO THE OTHER ACROSS THE NAPE AND THEN, USING THE SCALPEL, THE SKIN IS CAREFULLY PEELED ALL THE WAY TO THE FRONT IN ONE SINGLE PIECE.

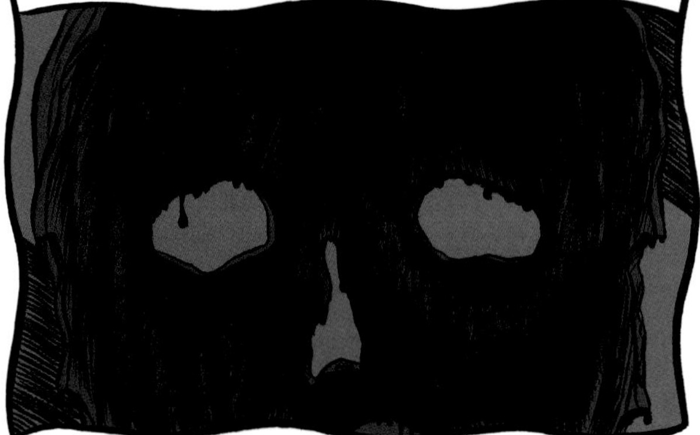
THE FACE IS MORE COMPLICATED. AN INCISION IS MADE UNDER THE CHIN TO BOTH EARS. YOU MUST BE SURE TO CUT PRECISELY AROUND THE EYES AND THE MOUTH BEFORE PULLING THE SKIN, OTHERWISE IT ALL RIPS OFF AND YOU'RE LEFT WITH A BLOODY MESS THAT IS DIFFICULT TO WORK WITH. THE SKIN IS PULLED UNTIL IT REACHES THE FOREHEAD AND IS REMOVED. IT LOOKS LIKE A MASK OF SKIN WITH HOLES FOR THE EYES AND THE MOUTH.

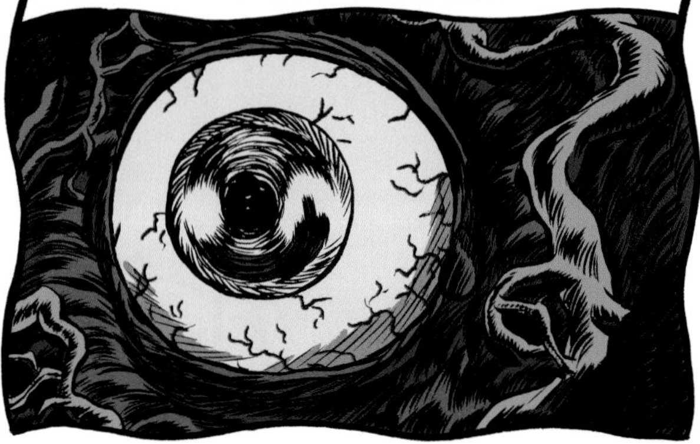
YOU CAN THEN SEVER THE LIPS AND THE EYELIDS. THE VICTIM LOSES CONSCIOUSNESS IN THE INTERIM. I AM COUNTING ON YOUR EXPERTISE TO CONSTANTLY BRING HIM BACK. THE FACE IS HARD TO LOOK AT. THE TEETH ARE EXPOSED, AND TWO BIG WHITE GLOBES STARE BACK AT YOU FROM A MESSY, BLOODY PULP. IT'S FRIGHTENING, BUT, IN THE CASE OF OUR BEAST HERE, HE'S ALREADY PRETTY UGLY.

AT THIS POINT, THE FLOOR IS A VERITABLE POOL OF BLOOD. YOU MUST CONCENTRATE ON WHAT YOU ARE DOING. NEXT, THE TORSO IS SKINNED; IT'S RELATIVELY EASY AFTER THE FACE. THE SKIN IS REMOVED IN ONE PIECE AS WELL. BUT I HAVE RARELY GOTTEN TO THAT POINT. THE VICTIM HAS BEEN SPILLING HIS GUTS FOR A WHILE. HE THEN DIES FROM HEMORRHAGING. HE'S STILL TALKING BUT ONLY IN ORDER TO END HIS SUFFERING. HE WILL SOMETIMES SAY ANYTHING OR MAY BECOME INAUDIBLE THROUGH THE SCREAMING AND VOMITING.

HE'S ALL YOURS, DOCTOR.

CLING!
CLING!
CLOSED

CLIC

HELLO.

HELLO.
MADAM.

HOW MANY ROOMS?
UH... WHERE ARE WE EXACTLY?

AT THE HOTEL, SIR.
YES, YES, OBVIOUSLY. BUT I MEAN...
IN WHICH REGION EXACTLY?
REGION?
IS THIS THE COUNTRYSIDE?

THE COUNTRYSIDE? HOW DID YOU GET HERE?
THERE! BY THE LADDER! IT IS THE COUNTRYSIDE OUTSIDE, ISN'T IT?

YOU DON'T KNOW WHERE YOU ARE, SO THAT'S GOOD, ISN'T IT?
WE'RE KILLING OURSELVES TRYING TO TELL YOU!

"WE'RE KILLING OURSELVES."

THIS PLACE IS HERE. IT'S NOT THE CITY AND IT'S NOT THE COUNTRYSIDE. IT'S NOT FACT AND IT'S NOT FICTION. IT IS TIME PASSING. A REFUGE. WE ARE INVISIBLE. EVEN TO OURSELVES. YOU WILL SEE. YOU'LL GET USED TO IT.

DINNER IS SERVED AT 8 P.M. IN THE DINING HALL.

DINING ROOM

THE TAPESTRY IS BECOMING A LITTLE UNDONE.
SO AM I.

YAWN

I'M GOING TO BED.

SO ARE WE.

WHAT'S YOUR SICKNESS LIKE?

WHAT?! HOW DO YOU...

THEY SAID THAT YOU FALL INTO A KOMA SOMETIMES.

"THEY"?
WHO IS "THEY"?

WELL.
US.

YOU?

YES, US... WE TOLD OURSELVES THAT YOU FREQUENTLY WENT INTO A KOMA.

OH?
WHAT'S IT LIKE?

WELL, IT'S AS IF AN EMPTY BUBBLE EXPLODED IN MY HEAD. AN EXPLOSION OF NOTHING. BUT IT'S MOSTLY THIS COLD THAT SWEEPS OVER ME AND THIS BIZARRE FEELING LIKE I'M DISAPPEARING.
AND IT'S WHITE! ALL WHITE!

WHITE?
WHAT? YOU WOULD HAVE PREFERRED BLACK?

NO... I MEAN, WHITE IS AT LEAST SOMETHING... BLACK IS EVEN LESS, NOTHING AT ALL.

IT'S A MATTER OF OPINION.
PROBABLY, PROBABLY.

I TOLD YOU IT WAS WHITE.
I DON'T REMEMBER THAT.

ARE YOU SICK AS WELL?
IT'S BEEN A LONG TIME.
IN SHORT, WE ARE HERE TO HEAL.
IT'S GOOD THAT YOU REALIZE THAT.

I WONDER HOW EXACTLY THIS PLACE CAN HEAL ANYTHING...EVEN A COLD, BUT WHATEVER!

IT'S ODD THAT ALL THREE OF US ARE HERE.
I MEAN, WE ALL HAVE THE SAME ILLNESS, NO? AND YOU PROBABLY DON'T HAVE ANY EPISODES HERE, RIGHT?
NOT HERE, NO.

WE CAN'T KNOW THAT WE ARE DIFFERENT WHEN WE ARE CHILDREN. BUT WE DO KNOW. IT'S A PROBLEM FOR OTHERS. WE DON'T HAVE A PROBLEM BEING AROUND OTHER PEOPLE, WE CAN TAKE THEM BY THE HAND, TALK TO THEM, PLAY WITH THEM. BUT FOR THEM, IT'S AS IF THEY ARE AFRAID TO GET HURT, OR TO INFLICT HURT. IT MAKES EVERYTHING TOO COMPLICATED. AND SO, IN THEIR EYES, YOU BECOME A PROBLEM. NO EATING ICE CREAM WITHOUT A PROBLEM. NO GOING TO THE MOVIES WITHOUT A PROBLEM...

I WANTED TO GO TO THE COUNTRYSIDE. MAYBE THIS REALLY IS IT; I MUST GO AND FIND MY FRIEND AND FIND THIS PLACE AGAIN.

I'M WINSTON.
SHE'S SHELL.

ADDIDAS.
BUT NOT LIKE THE SHOES, OKAY?

YOU DO KNOW THAT YOUR MACHINES ARE UNPLUGGED?

?!

FT...

FT...
SHH...

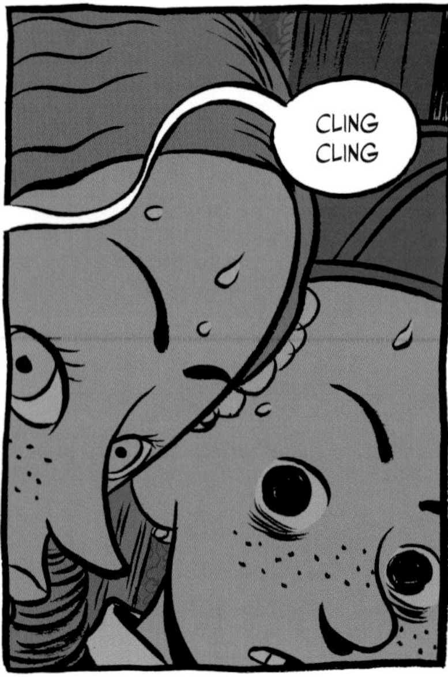
CLING CLING

COME ON!
IT'S HIM!
HIM?

HE'S VERY DANGEROUS.

MORE DANGEROUS THAN YOU CAN IMAGINE!

IS HE BIG? RED WITH HORNS?
LIKE THE ONES DOWN THERE?
I HAVE NO IDEA WHAT YOU'RE TALKING ABOUT.
ALL I CAN TELL YOU IS THAT HE LOOKS LIKE NOTHING YOU'VE EVER IMAGINED BEFORE.
DON'T... DON'T LOOK AT HIM, EVER!
DON'T EVER LOOK AT HIM!

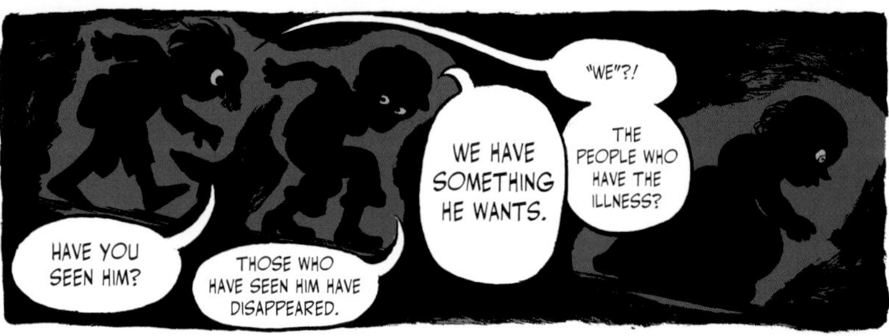
HAVE YOU SEEN HIM?
THOSE WHO HAVE SEEN HIM HAVE DISAPPEARED.
WE HAVE SOMETHING HE WANTS.
"WE"?!
THE PEOPLE WHO HAVE THE ILLNESS?

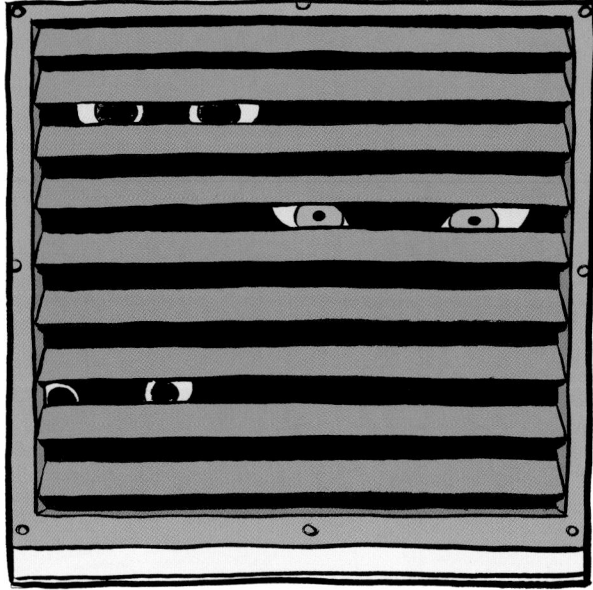

THERE WERE OTHER CHILDREN LIKE US HERE. WE'RE THE LAST ONES.
AND HE SOMETIMES COMES TO SEE IF THERE ARE ANY LEFT.

WHAT NUMBER?
310.
CRAP! WRONG HALLWAY!

WHAT ABOUT YOU?
8.

WHAT IS THIS PLACE?

HURRY UP!

3,785?
THERE ARE 3,000 ROOMS IN THIS HOTEL?
3785

HE'S ALREADY THERE!
B2.

THIS WAY!

CLANK

HURRY!
?

WE ALL HAVE TO GO THROUGH THE DOORWAY AT THE SAME TIME!

AH!
CRASH

ROOM 5! WE CAN MAKE IT!

GRUMBLE... WHAT'S GOING ON?

ADDIDAS? WHAT ARE YOU...
DAD! YOU HAVE TO HIDE! THERE'S A...

HE'S FINE. IT'S NOT THEM HE'S AFTER!

SHLIK

HURRY!

SCRITCH... SCRITCH
CLAC

ADDI...

WELL, I COULD HAVE SWORN THAT...
THAT THIS ROOM WAS...

DID YOU LOCK IT?
OF COURSE.

HE'LL BE BACK. HE SAW US.
AND I GUESS WE CAN'T LEAVE THIS HOTEL?
HMM.

I GOT HERE THROUGH A HOLE BY A LADDER!
YOU'LL NEVER FIND IT AGAIN!

SO, WE'RE STUCK HERE UNTIL THAT THING FINDS US.
WE'VE ALWAYS GOTTEN AWAY UNTIL NOW. WE'VE PERFECTED A LOT OF TRICKS.

WE MADE KEYS FOR EVERY ROOM. AND EVERY TIME HE COMES, WE HIDE IN A NEW ONE.
BY THE TIME HE TRIES ALL THE KEYS...

YOU'VE MADE COPIES FOR *3,000* ROOMS?

THERE AREN'T ACTUALLY 3,000 ROOMS; IT'S A BIT...FAR-FETCHED.
I DON'T THINK HE KNEW HOW MANY WE WERE GOING TO BE.
YES, SOMETIMES THE NUMBER ISN'T THE SAME AS THE ONE ON THE KEYS. SO WE USE OTHER TRICKS.

"HE DIDN'T KNOW HOW MANY WE WERE GOING TO BE."
YOU MEAN THAT *HE* BUILT THIS PLACE?

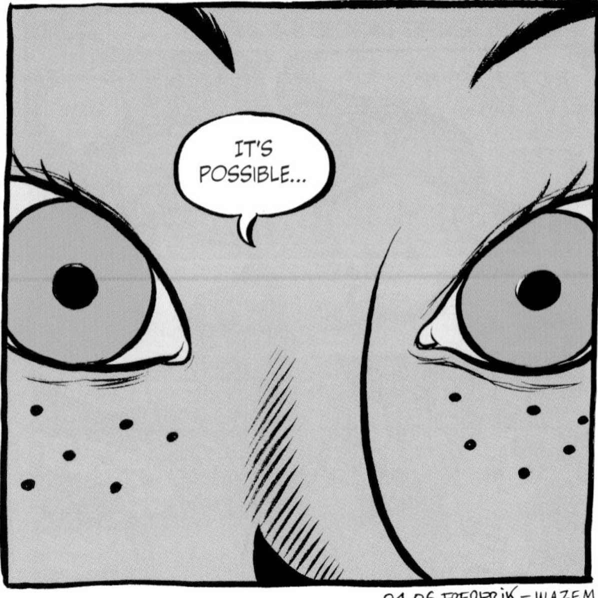

IT'S POSSIBLE...

01.06 FREDERIK-WAZEM

TCHAK

GODDAMN IT
GODDAMN IT
GODDAMN IT...

EVERYTHING OKAY, COMMISSIONER?

GODDAMN IT
GODDAMN IT
GODDAMN IT...

I REFUSE TO PERISH IN THIS PLACE!
I HAVE TO GET OUT OF HERE.
TCHAK
...IF I WANT MY OPINION...
TCHAK
TCHAK
TCHAK
TCHAK
TCHAK

I KNOW I SAW THAT MONSTER!
I SAW IT!

IT'S A CONSPIRACY!
TSHAK

BRRROOM

PING!

GODDAMN IT GODDAMN IT GODDAMN IT GODDAMN IT...

MAKE IT QUICK, DOCTOR.

I...
I'M SORRY.

I BEG YOU!... TELL THEM WHAT THEY WANT TO KNOW.
I BEG YOU!

PLIC

THERE... NOW YOU HAVE TO PEEL THE SKIN ON EITHER SIDE...
IT USUALLY COMES AWAY QUITE EASILY.
Fsst

THIS IS A FIRST WITH AN ANIMAL OF THIS KIND, RIGHT?
MM-HMM.

ALLLL THE WAY DOWN TO THE WRIST...
I BEG YOU...

DRiiiiiiNG! ...

IT HAPPENED...
IT HAPPENED ?!!

CONTACT!

READY THE ROBOTS. SEND THE REGIMENT DOWN! NOW!
SHOOT ON SIGHT!

WE HAVE LIMITED TIME TO REPLACE THE CREATURES WITH OUR MACHINES...
THE BEASTS WILL MOST ASSUREDLY ABANDON US ONE BY ONE.

IF I'M THE FIRST TO FALTER... YOU'LL PLUG ME BACK IN, WON'T YOU?
AND YOU'LL DO THE SAME!

PLIC
PLOC

WELL...
OKAY!
I BETTER SEW YOU BACK UP THEN...

SO, THERE'S NOTHING WE CAN DO OTHER THAN TRY AND ESCAPE FOREVER.
MM-HMM.
WHILE WE'RE LOCKED UP HERE, RIGHT?
WELL, YEAH.

HOW LONG HAVE YOU TWO BEEN HERE?

PFFTT...
A PRETTY LONG TIME!
IT'S AS IF THE CLOCK WAS BROKEN AND EVERYTHING WAS OFF-KILTER.

HMM.
MAYBE IT'S JUST STOPPED.
WHAT?
THE CLOCK! NOT BROKEN... JUST STOPPED.
WHAT DOES THAT CHANGE?

YEAH.

AND IF WE CAN'T GET OUT, CAN MY FATHER AND THE MCMULLANS GET OUT?
NO. NO ONE CAN GET OUT! NO... THEY'LL JUST LOSE THEIR MEMORY AND ASSUME A ROLE IN THIS HOTEL...
LIKE THE RECEPTIONIST...SHE WASN'T A RECEPTIONIST WHEN SHE FIRST GOT HERE...
SHE BECAME ONE LITTLE BY LITTLE.

ARE THERE ANY OTHERS?
NO... US, YOUR FATHER, HIS FRIENDS AND THE RECEPTIONIST.
THERE HAVE NEVER BEEN THIS MANY ADULTS HERE.

WE HAVE TO GET OUT THEN!

YEAH!

AND THE ONLY WAY TO GET OUT...
IS TO FACE HIM.

HE'S CLEVER.
REALLY?
IT'S LIKE IN THE WESTERNS. WHEN YOU LOSE YOUR HORSE, YOU HAVE TWO OPTIONS: YOU EITHER CHASE HIM, UNSURE YOU'LL EVEN CATCH HIM, OR YOU SIT BY THE BRIDGE NEAR THE WATER AND YOU WAIT...

WAIT FOR WHAT?

WAIT UNTIL HE GETS THIRSTY!

I THINK IF YOU'RE SMART, YOU'LL WAIT...
AND HE'S CRAFTY BECAUSE HE BUILT THE BRIDGE.
THIS HOTEL?
EXACTLY!
HE KNEW WE'D COME HERE.

HMM.

OKAY, LET'S GO!
BUT...
WHERE?!

I'M GOING TO SAY GOODBYE TO MY DAD AND WHEN THAT THING COMES BACK, WE DON'T HIDE FROM IT.

NO...

NO?

WE CAN'T DO THAT, WE CAN'T DO THAT...
WE'VE BEEN RUNNING FOR SO LONG...
ALL RIGHT, TAKE CARE OF MY DAD THEN. I'LL COME BACK FOR YOU.

BUT, NO ONE HAS EVER COME BACK!
MAYBE THEY DIDN'T HAVE A REASON TO RETURN!

OPEN THE DOOR.

8

UM...
HOW DO I...
THIS IS THE BASEMENT!
JUST TAKE THE ELEVATOR AT THE END THERE.

I'LL BE BACK...

ADDIDAS!

DON'T JUDGE US...
I...
IT'S NOT EASY FOR US...

BREAKFAST IS SERVED IN THE DINING HALL, GENTLEMEN...

SAY...
HAVE YOU SEEN MY DAUGHTER?

SHE'S PLAYING WITH THE OTHER TWO CHILDREN, SIR.

HMM.

DID YOU NOTICE THE RECEPTIONIST...
UM...
SHE...
YEAH.

IT'S KIND OF STRANGE, NO?
I DON'T KNOW ANYMORE.
"YOU DON'T KNOW ANYMORE," WHAT?

WHAT'S STRANGE...
...AND WHAT ISN'T MEANT TO BE...

OKAY...
BUT REALLY!
HOLY COW!
YOU TOO!

WHAT, WHAT "ME TOO"?!?
YOU LOOK DIFFERENT, DAD!

GOD HELP ME, IT'S NOT TRUE...
WHAT?!
NOW IT'S YOU!

WELL, DON'T LOOK AT ME LIKE THAT!
I'M NOT GOING TO CHANGE!
THAT'S TOTALLY UNLIKE ME!

WHY US AND NOT YOU?
'CAUSE...
'CAUSE I DON'T JUST CHANGE LIKE THAT! THAT'S ALL!

DOES IT HURT?...

NO...WE DON'T FEEL ANYTHING... RIGHT?
NO...WE DON'T FEEL ANYTHING AT ALL.

SAY...DID I RETURN TO NORMAL?
HMM...
YES, YES, OF COURSE.
IT ONLY LASTED A SECOND.

WHAT ABOUT ME?
YUP...
NO PROBLEM!

YEAH...
BACK TO YOURSELF!
THE SAME UGLY MUG!
HA HA...

OH!
HOLY...

WHAT?
NO!
DID I CHANGE?
DID I CHANGE?

CRAP!
YEAH!
YOU CAN SAY THAT AGAIN!

THAT'S IT... ENOUGH!
LET'S GO!
EVERYONE OUT!

YOU...
I'M NOT TALKING TO YOU!

RATTLE...

RATTLE RATTLE RATTLE RATTLE

YOU WILL OPEN THIS DOOR THIS INSTANT!

IT'S LOCKED FROM THE OUT-SIDE, SIR.
IT'S LOCKED FROM THE OUTSIDE?!
FROM THE OUTSIDE, SIR...

WE CAME IN THAT DOOR LAST NIGHT... HMM... I THINK... AND IT WAS OPEN!
OF COURSE, OF COURSE...
BUT IT'S LOCKED FROM THE OUTSIDE... EVERYTHING! EVERYTHING IS LOCKED FROM THE OUTSIDE!

OH YEAH?!

WELL, YOU MAY NOT KNOW THIS, LITTLE LADY, BUT MY DAUGHTER TWEAKED MY MACHINE!
AND SHE MADE ME SUPER STRONG! A SUPERMAN!

A FORCE TO BE RECKONED WITH!
HA HAA!
A KILLING MACHINE!

HMPH...

HA!!!

CRASH

WE HAVE TO GET OUT OF HERE!
WE HAVE THINGS TO DO...
THERE...
OUT THERE...

RIGHT, MCMULLAN?
TELL HER!

AH
UM...
YES.
THAT'S TRUE.

AAAA
I DON'T WANT TO STAY HERE!

YOU'RE NOTHING HERE AND YOU WILL ADAPT VERY QUICKLY. IT'S QUITE HANDY. YOU DON'T HAVE TO THINK AND YOU DON'T HAVE TO ACCOUNT FOR YOUR ACTIONS.
YOU'LL SEE...

I DON'T REMEMBER VERY WELL EITHER... BUT I WASN'T A RECEPTIONIST OR A CHAMBERMAID, OR A BUTLER... I WAS SOMETHING ELSE... SOMEONE...
IT'S LIKELY THAT YOU WILL SIMPLY BECOME HOTEL GUESTS OF SOME SORT.
GUESTS??

YES.
ALL KINDS OF CLIENTS. YOU WON'T EVEN KNOW... AND IT DOESN'T HURT WHEN YOU LOSE YOUR MEMORY...
THERE IS NOTHING TO LEAVE, NOTHING TO FORGET...
AND NOTHING TO REGRET.

BUT I DON'T WANT TO BECOME A CLIENT!
NO, NO, NO, NO!
I AM NOT A CLIENT!
I AM JULIUS EME. NOT A CLIENT OF THIS DAMN HOTEL.
GIVE ME A PEN AND A PIECE OF PAPER!

THANK YOU.
SCRITCH SCRICH

THERE!
-JULIUS EME
-CHIMNEY SWEEP
(SON OF LEONARD EME, HUSBAND OF ROSITA EME AND FATHER OF ADDIDAS EME)

HAAA...
TAKES YOUR BREATH AWAY, DOESN'T IT?

YES...THAT IS QUITE CLEVER, ACTUALLY...
I SHOULD HAVE DONE THAT MYSELF.

AND WHO SAYS YOU DIDN'T?

YOU SHOULDN'T PUT THAT IN YOUR POCKET.
REALLY?
WHY NOT?

BECAUSE OF THAT...

GOD DAMN...
HELLO...
A ROOM, PLEASE...
FOR THE NIGHT.

DAMN!
AH! THERE WE GO...

TAKE THIS AND PUT IT SOMEWHERE SAFE...
OF COURSE, SIR.

WHAT'S THIS?

DID YOU SEE THAT?
STRANGE.

BUT?!
WHAT...?

INCREDIBLE!
WHO...
WHO WROTE THIS?!

AHEM...
MY KEY, PLEASE.

BLAM
BLAM
N40

BLAM
ARGH!

tac
tac
tac

BLAM
BLAM

23

RRRRRRRRRRRR
RRRRRR
RRRRR
RRRR R R

RRRRRRRRRRRR

CRASH

BROOOOOM

AAAH!

POUF

PLAF

YOU!
ERP.

G...

FLOUP..

WHAT THE...

I DON'T UNDERSTAND! MY MEN ARE FALLING LIKE FLIES!
JUST LIKE THAT! ALL OF A SUDDEN!
I...

DID YOU COME FROM THE FRONT LINES?
FROM THE FRONT? THEY'RE... THEY'RE USING
GAS...
THEY...

CRRRRR
GODDAM...

AAAAA

PLAF!!
OUCH!

MMMMPH...

?!

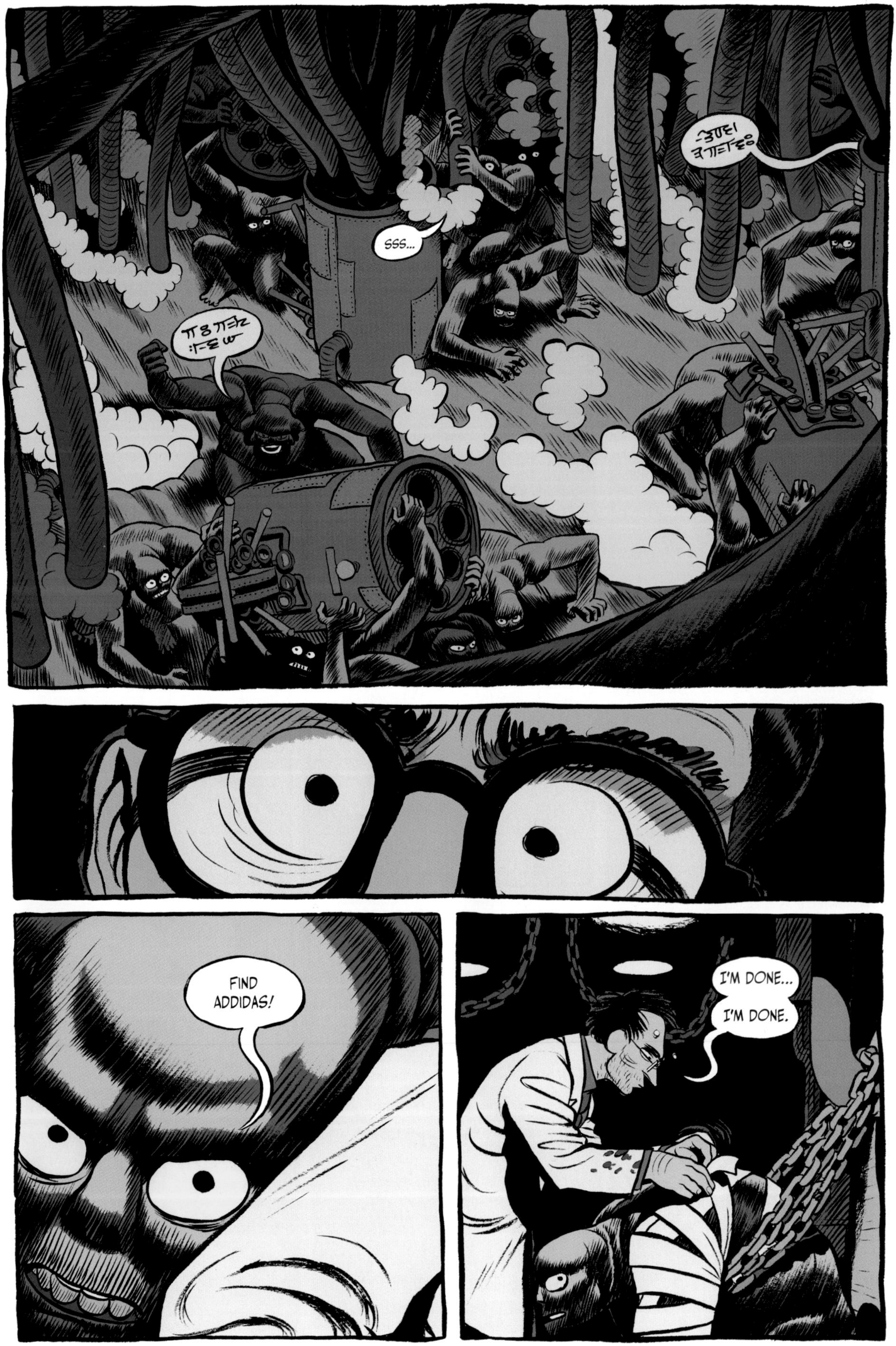

SSS...

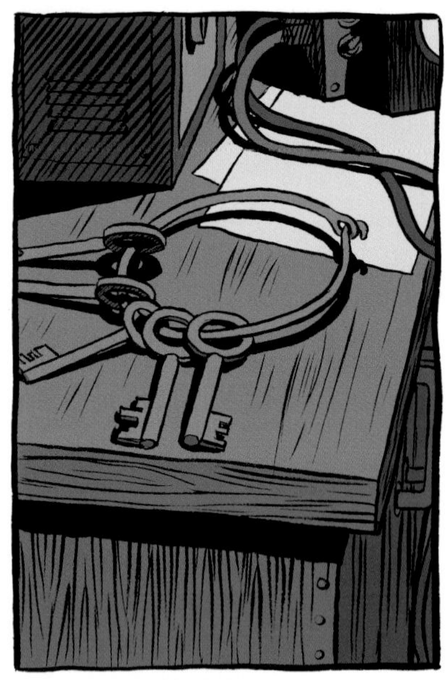

HM.
THERE.

IF I UNTIE YOU...
YOU...
YOU WON'T HURT ME...
...WILL YOU?
SCRATCH SCRATCH

NO.

SHLING

I...
I AM NOT REALLY...
I MEAN.
I'M A COWARD, YOU KNOW...
BUT I...

MUST FIND ADDIDAS!

OH, YES, YES...
OF COURSE, OF COURSE...
THE GIRL.
CLICK CLICK

SHLINGLINGLING
SHLIGLI SHLING
SHLING SHLING

I'M AMAZED...
EVERYONE IS KILLING THEMSELVES TO TRY AND FIND THIS LITTLE GIRL!

PLOTCH

?!

SSSSSSSS

ZZZZZ...

ZZZ...

BANK
PLAF

...YOU BE LIKE THEM SOON.
OH.
REALLY.
IF YOU SAY SO.
EVERYONE...
UH-HUH.

...EXCEPT ADDIDAS.
REALLY!

CLEARLY, THAT GIR--
UH...

pouf..

ZZ...

DAMN IT, MCMULLAN, CAN'T YOU READ WHAT'S WRITTEN THERE??
YOU ARE MISTAKEN, SIR... YOU HAVE MISTAKEN ME FOR SOMEONE ELSE.

DON'T BE AN IDIOT, MCMULLAN. READ THIS!

RO-SI-TA...
...EME...

JULIUS...
IT'S...
YOUR WIFE WROTE THIS!

WHO WROTE THIS?!

IT'S QUITE POSSIBLE THAT I DID.
IN ANY CASE,
IT IS MY WRITING...

ARE YOU LISTENING, JULIUS? DO YOU UNDERSTAND WHAT THIS MEANS?

EXCUSE ME MADAM, BUT I BELIEVE I HAVE SOME ITEMS HERE THAT COULD BE OF INTEREST TO YOU.
POUF

FOR CHRIST'S SAKE, JULIUS, *OPEN YOUR EYES!*
BAF

READ-THIS-YOU-DAMN-IDIOT-READ-IT!
LOOK!

ROSITA...

EME...
...

IT'S HER...
DAMN IT...
IT'S HER.

AH...
IT'S ME.

HMM...
YES.
YES.

THAT'S IT...

GOOD.

WHAT DO WE DO NOW?

tac tac
tac tac tac

PUFF...

ZZ...
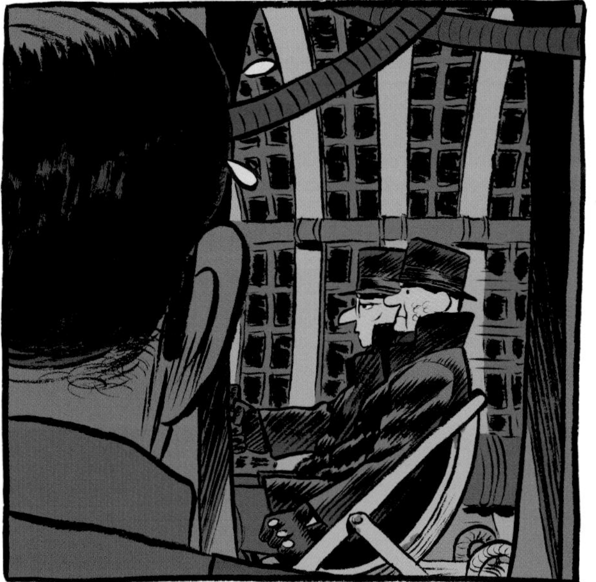

uuuuuuuuuuuuuu
27

HEY!

HEY!
WAIT!
UUUUUU
H103

PUF
PUF
PUF
PUF
PUF

STOP!
PUFF PUFF
STOP!

SO?
NO BIG MONSTERS, EH?!

I SAW IT...
PUFF PUFF
I AM NOT CRAZY!
PUFF
IT'S A CONSPIRACY.

NOW IS NOT THE TIME!

THE PIT...
THE MACHINES!
YOU KNEW ALL ABOUT IT, YOU GODDAMN ...

LET IT GO, OLD MAN!

WHIRRR

WHAT-IS-THE-DEAL-WITH-ALL-THIS-CRAZINESS?!!

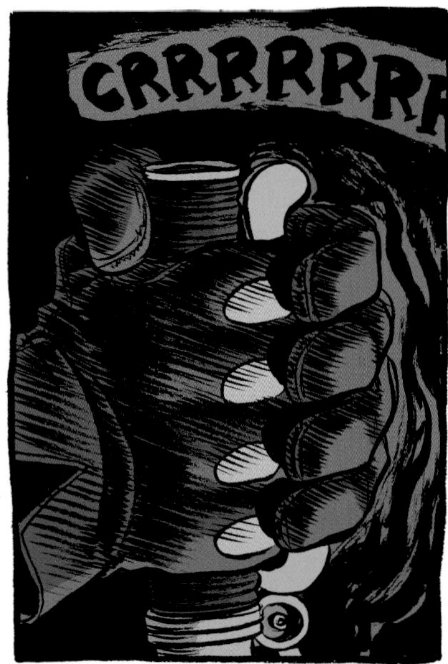
CRRRRRRRR

CRRAASH

YOU...

...WITH ME.

AHHHH NO! LEAVE ME ALONE.

AHHHH!

HELP!
HELP ME!

I DON'T WANT TO DIE!

NOOOOOO...

...OOOOOO!!!

BOOOM!

SKOUIK

KLANK
?!

III
III

COME OUT!
I...
I KNOW WHO YOU ARE.

III...

HAVE YOU EVER WATCHED A WESTERN?

THE COWBOYS, GUNMEN, PISTOLEROS, THEY COULD SHOOT LIKE GODS. THEY WERE ONE WITH THEIR GUNS.
BUT NOT ONE OF THEM COULD FABRICATE ONE...

DRIP
PLIC...

IT'S ONE THING TO WIELD A WEAPON. IT'S QUITE ANOTHER TO FABRICATE ONE.
YOU HAVE TO ATTEMPT TO COPY THE ORIGINAL MODEL. TO BUILD IT EXACTLY. UNDERSTAND THE MECHANICS AND REPRODUCE THEM... NOT EASY, IS IT?... IT CAN SOMETIMES HAPPEN THAT THE FINAL PRODUCT DOESN'T MIRROR THE ORIGINAL, THAT IT IS DEFECTIVE...
OR...
...BETTER THAN THE ORIGINAL!

DO YOU WANT TO KNOW WHY I LIKE WESTERNS SO MUCH?

BECAUSE IT DOESN'T EXIST, IT HAS NEVER EXISTED AND ELUDES YOU COMPLETELY... IT'S OUTSIDE OF YOU! IT'S A STORY...
AND DO YOU KNOW HOW THE STORIES END?
DO YOU? DO YOU?...

...WITH A DUEL...

YOU BUILT THE MACHINES, DIDN'T YOU?
...YOU CREATED US?...
...YOU WANTED TO MAKE US IN YOUR IMAGE, BUT YOU FAILED. THE OUTCOME HAS FAR EXCEEDED THE MODEL AND SOME, LIKE ME, BROKE AWAY FROM YOU!

THAT IS EXACTLY RIGHT, MISS.

THE OUTCOME EXCEEDED THE PROJECTED MODEL... TO THE POINT, MISS, THAT YOU CANNOT EVEN IMAGINE!

I DON'T KNOW HOW YOU BECAME SO INDEPENDENT, YOU AND THOSE OTHER CHILDREN; YOU ARE AN ACCIDENT OF SOME SORT...A VIRUS...

I DON'T THINK IT'S POSSIBLE TO CREATE SOMETHING AND NOT HAVE AN ELEMENT ELUDE YOU.

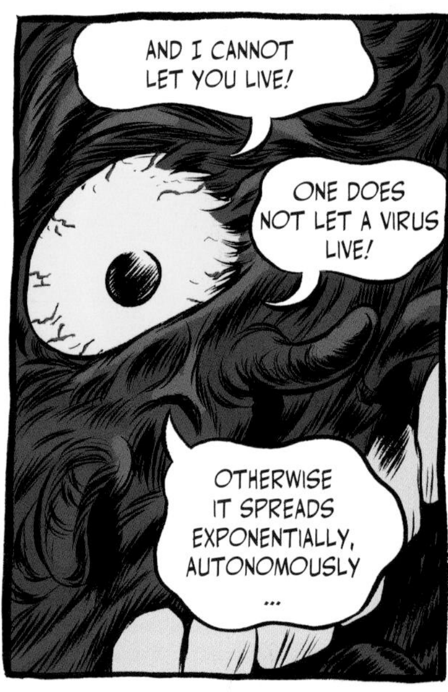

IT'S ONE THING TO STOP THE CLOCK...
IT'S ANOTHER TO STOP TIME ...
BELIEVE ME.

WE ARE NO LONGER IN YOUR DREAM!
IT'S NOT YOUR STORY ANY LONGER, IT'S MINE!

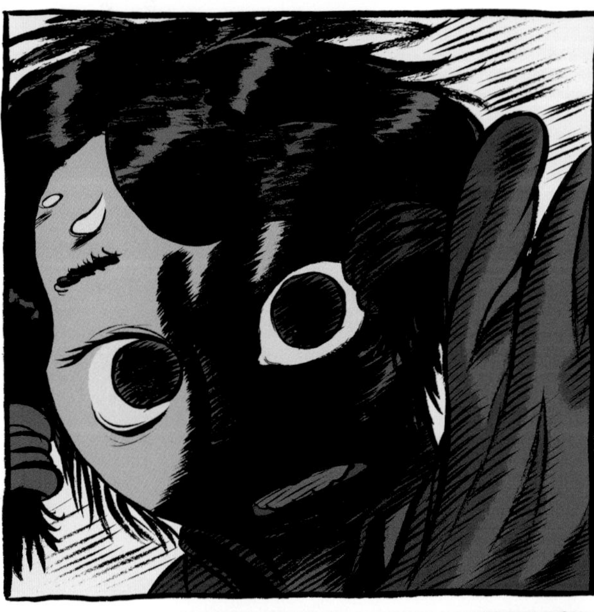

BAF

GH...

SNRF

SSSSSSSSSS

PLAF

COUGH-
COUGH-
COUGH...

SIGH.

WHERE ARE WE?

IN A PLACE YOU DID NOT IMAGINE!

SSSSSSSSS

IF YOU KILL ME HERE...
YOU CAN NEVER GET OUT!

SSSSSSSSS

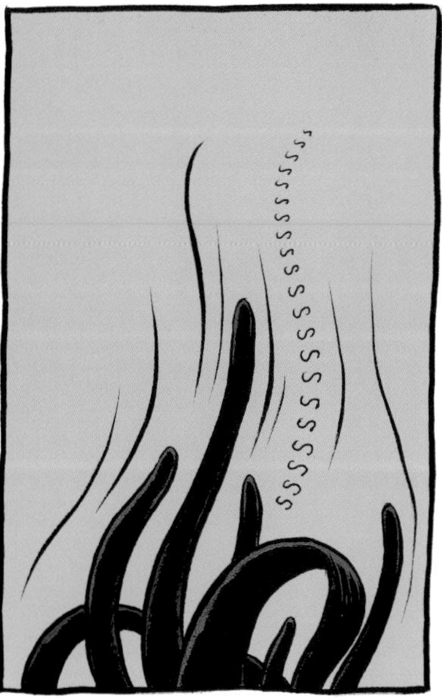
SSSSSSSSSSSSSSSSSSSSS

02.07 FREDERIK WAZEM

SQUIBB
SANKA
CAFE

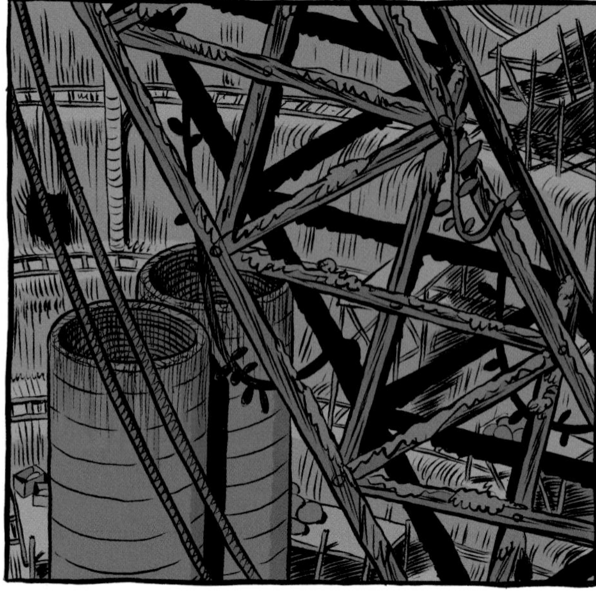

YOU WON'T STOP, EH? RIGHT?? YOU WON'T STOP??
DAMN IT! YOU BETTER NOT EITHER!

IDIOTS! IF ONE OF US STOPS, ONE OF US DROPS.
AND IF ONE OF US DROPS... WE ALL DROP!

YES, YES... OBVIOUSLY, OBVIOUSLY.
OBVIOUSLY!

WHAT ABOUT SLEEP?
HOW DO WE SLEEP AND EAT AND EVERYTHING?

WHAT DO WE DO TO SLEEP?
NO SLEEP!
NO EAT, NO POOP!

YOU'RE TRYING TO KILL US! YOU GOD DAMN...

WE'RE GOING TO DIE! HE WANTS TO KILL US ALL! OF EXHAUSTION...
FOR THE LOVE OF GOD, WATCH OUT!

THE...
THE...
LEVER...
AAAA

!!

PUFF
PUFF
PUFF

HUP!
PUFF
HUP!
HUP!
PUFF

SIGH

HOW DID YOU KNOW ABOUT ALL THIS?
SHUT UP!

SHUT UP?
YEAH! SHUT IT!

I DON'T THINK YOU'VE QUITE UNDERSTOOD OUR SITUATION...

...AND I'M BUT THE *LITTLE* COMMISSIONER, AND YOU'RE THE OH-SO-IMPORTANT OFFICIALS!!! I AM GOING TO ASK YOU AGAIN, AND IF I DO NOT GET A SATISFACTORY ANSWER...
...I'LL STOP!
GOOD-BYE, GENTLEMEN, WE ARE DONE!

AS I WAS SAYING.
HOW DID YOU KNOW ABOUT ALL THIS?

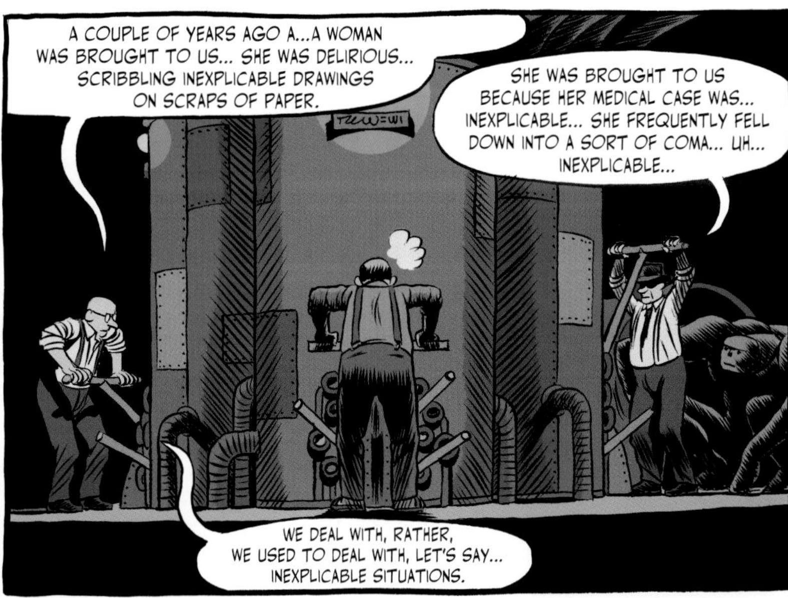
A COUPLE OF YEARS AGO A...A WOMAN WAS BROUGHT TO US... SHE WAS DELIRIOUS... SCRIBBLING INEXPLICABLE DRAWINGS ON SCRAPS OF PAPER.
SHE WAS BROUGHT TO US BECAUSE HER MEDICAL CASE WAS... INEXPLICABLE... SHE FREQUENTLY FELL DOWN INTO A SORT OF COMA... UH... INEXPLICABLE...
WE DEAL WITH, RATHER, WE USED TO DEAL WITH, LET'S SAY... INEXPLICABLE SITUATIONS.

IS THERE A LINK BETWEEN THE WOMAN AND THE LITTLE GIRL AND HER MONSTER?

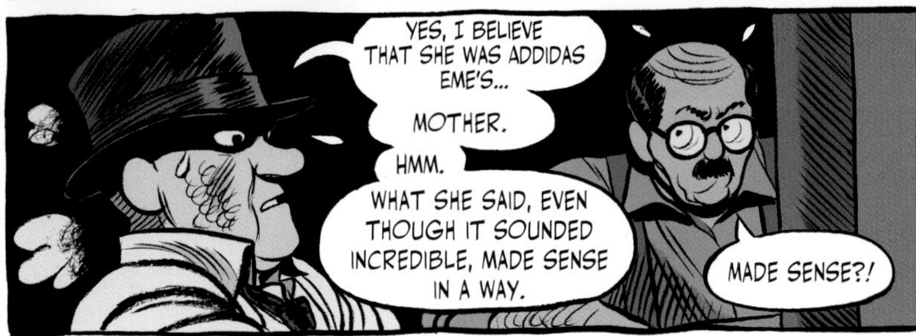
YES, I BELIEVE THAT SHE WAS ADDIDAS EME'S...
MOTHER.
HMM.
WHAT SHE SAID, EVEN THOUGH IT SOUNDED INCREDIBLE, MADE SENSE IN A WAY.
MADE SENSE?!

LET'S SAY THAT IT HELD UP.
IN A WAY.
SHE BEGAN TO GRADUALLY WITHDRAW LITTLE BY LITTLE FROM OUR QUESTIONS.

HER DRAWINGS REPRESENTED A MONSTER, A MACHINE, AND THE DEPTHS OF EARTH...
WE WANTED TO FIND THE PLACE SHE HAD SEEN...
AND SHE DIDN'T WANT TO TELL US.

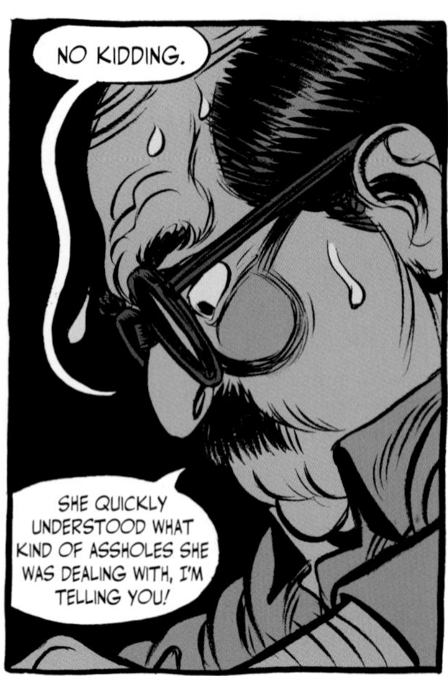
NO KIDDING.
SHE QUICKLY UNDERSTOOD WHAT KIND OF ASSHOLES SHE WAS DEALING WITH, I'M TELLING YOU!

WE... UM... WE INTERROGATED HER A LITTLE MORE.... FORCEFULLY.

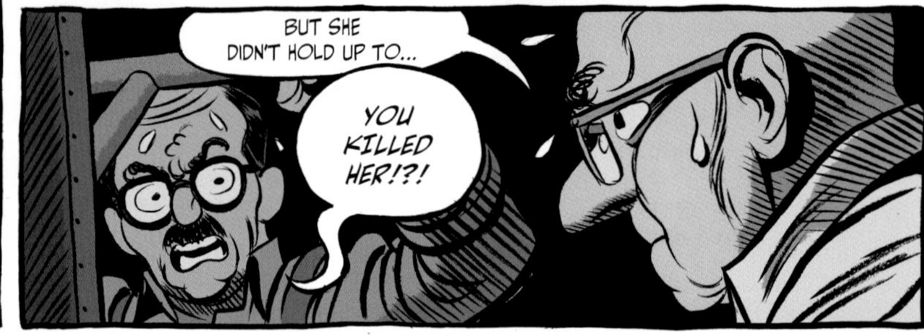
BUT SHE DIDN'T HOLD UP TO...
YOU KILLED HER!?!

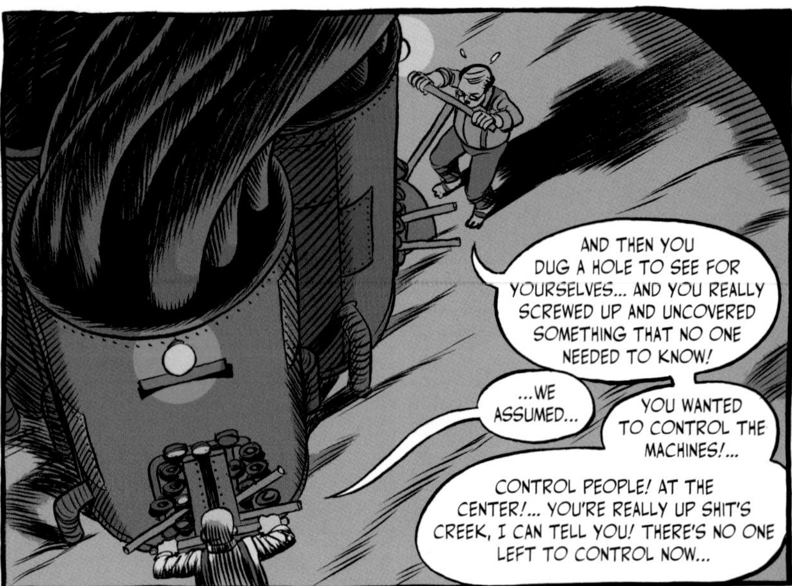
AND THEN YOU DUG A HOLE TO SEE FOR YOURSELVES... AND YOU REALLY SCREWED UP AND UNCOVERED SOMETHING THAT NO ONE NEEDED TO KNOW!
...WE ASSUMED...
YOU WANTED TO CONTROL THE MACHINES!...
CONTROL PEOPLE! AT THE CENTER!... YOU'RE REALLY UP SHIT'S CREEK, I CAN TELL YOU! THERE'S NO ONE LEFT TO CONTROL NOW...

SHIT, YOU REALLY SCREWED EVERYTHING UP! IF I COULD...
WE WANTED TO, BUT WE DIDN'T KNOW *HOW TO*... YES, WE WANTED TO CONTROL ALL THIS!
IMAGINE WHAT COULD HAPPEN IF IT FELL INTO THE WRONG HANDS!
IT DIDN'T NEED TO FALL INTO ANYONE'S HANDS!!

I'M GOING TO DECIDE WHEN TO STOP AND WHEN *I* DO, YOU'LL GO WITH ME.
YOU SEE, YOU NEVER CONTROLLED ANYTHING...
AND YOU DON'T EVEN HAVE CONTROL OVER YOUR OWN LIVES.

SAY...
UM...
WHERE ARE THE OTHERS?
ARE THERE STILL PEOPLE LEFT?

THIS WORLD FINISHED...

AND ALL YOUR...
THE ONES LIKE YOU?

FINISHED TOO...

WHERE IS THE LITTLE GIRL? ADDIDAS?

SIGH
ADDIDAS...

ADDIDAS...
WORLD AFTER FINISHED WORLD...

MCMULLAN!
SIR?

HEY! MCMULLAN!
HUH?
YES?
WHAT?
WHAT?
WHAT?

PLEASE GIVE ME TWO PIECES OF PAPER, ROSITA...

VERY GOOD, SIR.

THERE, NOW WRITE DOWN YOUR NAMES ...

SCRITCH SCRITCH

THERE.
NOW, GIVE THEM TO ROSITA...

PUT THEM WITH OURS IN THE CUBBY, WELL IN SIGHT.
HA HA! THIS IS AMAZING!

WE'RE GOING TO MEET A THOUSAND TIMES A DAY!
AHHH... ISN'T THAT GREAT?
ISN'T IT WONDERFUL?

PEOPLE MAKE PLANS FOR TOMOR-ROW...
BUT TOMORROW MAKES NO PLANS FOR THEM!
HA HA HA HA

WE DON'T CARE ABOUT TOMORROW. WE THUMB OUR NOSES AT TOMORROW!
WE'LL LIVE HERE FOR ALL ETERNITY AND WE'LL MEET AGAIN EVERY DAY AND WE'LL DANCE!

UPSADAISY!

TOMORROW DOESN'T EVEN KNOW WE EXIST...

GULP...

WHAT THE...

OH!
THAT!
YES.
THAT HAPPENS FROM TIME TO TIME...

SHE WAS LIKE THAT WHEN SHE ARRIVED.
?

THEN SHE CHANGED...
AND OFTEN!
YEAH.
PROBABLY BETTER THAT WAY.
WHAT ARE YOU DOING HERE?! WHERE IS ADDIDAS?! I THOUGHT SHE WAS WITH YOU!

OH!
UH...
BY THE WAY...
LET ME INTRODUCE MY WIFE.

YOUR WIFE?!!

I BEG YOUR PARDON?

YOU SAID, "YOUR WIFE"...
MAN, THIS IS GOING TO BE TOUGH TO EXPLAIN...

MADAM, WOULD YOU BE GOOD ENOUGH TO INTRODUCE ME TO THESE TWO TRICKSTERS?
SO?
THE ROOM?

THEY ARE CLIENTS, SIR... CLIENTS LIKE EVERYONE ELSE.
GOOD.
OKAY...
PSST.
GO PLAY! GO AND PLAY!

SAY... WHERE ARE WE EXACTLY?
AT THE HOTEL, SIR...

HMM... YES...OF COURSE... I'LL TAKE A ROOM THEN, PLEASE.
DINNER IS SERVED AT 8 P.M. IN THE DINING HALL.

GOOD, GOOD... I AM A LITTLE HUNGRY, ACTUALLY...
HMM.
SAY...
BY THE WAY...
DO I NORMALLY STAND ON THIS SIDE OF THE COUNTER?

JULIUS, WHAT ARE YOU DOING?! SHE'S YOUR WIFE!!
SIR?!

GIVE ME THOSE PAPERS THERE... IN THE CUBBY...

HERE.

LOOK! READ THIS PAPER, YOU DUMMY!
RO... SI... TA...

EME...
THERE!
SHE'S YOUR WIFE, I TELL YOU!

AND YOU, TOO! READ THIS!
OH... YES.
IT'S MY WRITING!

IT'S ME....
PFFT...
THIS IS EXHAUSTING.

YES?

THAT'S IT.

RIGHT, AS I WAS SAYING. ADDIDAS LEFT TO CONFRONT AND STOP ALL THIS MADNESS...
WE DIDN'T DARE FOLLOW HER BECAUSE WE HAVE BEEN HIDING FROM HIM FOR SO LONG...

BECAUSE HE WANTS TO BE RID OF US BECAUSE WE'RE NOT LIKE THE OTHERS AND HE THINKS WE COULD BE DANGEROUS... I DON'T SEE HOW WE CAN BE DANGEROUS, BUT I THINK THAT ADDIDAS MAY KNOW, SO SHE LEFT TO CONFRONT HIM AND SHE SAID, "HE'S CRAFTY BECAUSE HE BUILT THE BRIDGE (THIS PLACE). HE KNEW WE'D COME HERE."
US, THE CHILDREN, AT LEAST.
I DON'T GET WHAT *YOU'RE* DOING HERE...

SHE SAID, "IT'S LIKE WHEN YOU LOSE YOUR HORSE," UH, I CAN'T QUITE REMEMBER, "YOU WAIT UNTIL HE GETS THIRSTY..."
SOMETHING LIKE THAT...
WITH A THIRSTY HORSE...
YEAH...
ANYWAY, SHE'S WITH HIM!
THIS IS SERIOUS!

I DIDN'T UNDERSTAND A WORD YOU JUST SAID.
MADAM!
I CANNOT ABIDE ANIMAL ABUSE!
?

ESPECIALLY HORSE ABUSE! A HORSE IS A MAN'S BEST...
READ THIS!
INSTEAD OF RUNNING YOUR MOUTH.

SHE IS WITH WHO?
HERE, JIM.

DAD!
JIM!
INCREDIBLE!
THE CREATOR OF THIS... THIS WORLD, I THINK.

THE ONE WHO BUILT THE MACHINES?

WELL, I DON'T KNOW... WE NEVER SAW ANY MACHINES...
HE BUILT THIS HOTEL THING...
AND ALL THE OTHER THINGS...
...MAYBE...

WHAT IS SHE DOING GOING THERE?
HE... IS HE BAD?

SHE WENT TO CHANGE THINGS...
HE IS DANGEROUS.
BUT, IN A WAY...

I BELIEVE THAT SHE MAY BE MUCH MORE DANGEROUS THAN HE IS...

AND YOU REALLY BELIEVE THAT YOU CAN TELL ME THE END OF THE STORY!

I **WILL** TELL YOU THIS STORY... AND ON TOP OF THAT, YOU'RE NOT EVEN IN IT!

WHAT IS THIS PLACE CALLED?

IT'S CALLED *"THE COUNTRY-SIDE."*

FFFFFFF...

FSSHHHHHH

SSSSSSHHHHHAAA

GAAAAASP
...

AND NOW?
HOW DO YOU CALL THIS PLACE?
?!?

I CAN'T KILL YOU HERE, BUT YOU, YOU CAN'T LIVE HERE.
YOU CAN IMAGINE ALL YOU WANT. I WILL ALWAYS BE HERE TO DISTORT YOUR IMAGINATION...

YOU CAN TELL YOUR STORIES...
BUT I WILL ALWAYS BE THERE TO SPIN THEM MY WAY.

POUF

YOU SAID: "IT'S ONE THING TO STOP THE CLOCK...
IT'S ANOTHER TO STOP TIME..."

PUFF
PUFF

I WOULD RESPOND: "IT'S ONE THING TO TELL A STORY ...
IT'S ANOTHER TO KNOW WHEN TO LISTEN..."

SNRF

IT'S CALLED THE COUNTRYSIDE!!!

AS WE SPEAK, THERE ARE NO SURVIVORS... NO MORE ACTIVE MACHINES... THOSE LIKE ME HAVE GONE BACK TO THE DEPTHS OF THE EARTH NEVER TO RETURN.

EVEN IF YOU MANAGE TO KEEP ME HERE, YOU'LL NEVER BE ABLE TO BRING ANYONE BACK.

YOU CAN WANDER IN YOUR "COUNTRYSIDE" FOR ALL ETERNITY, BUT YOUR WORLD IS FINISHED...
I...

I WILL NOT KEEP YOU HERE...
I WILL *DESTROY* YOU...

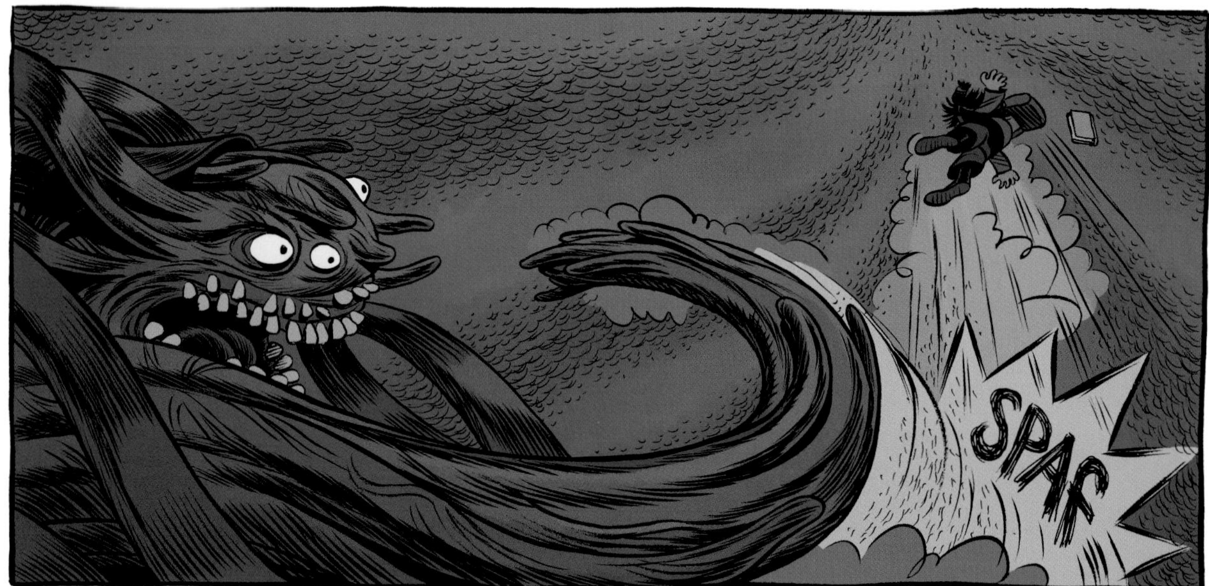
SPAF

FOR THAT...
YOU WILL...
NEED...
MORE IMAGINATION...

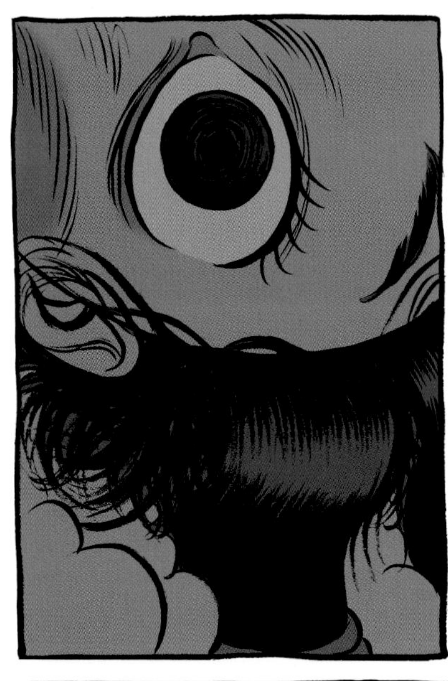

THAT'S IT...
THE KOMA...
IN A KOMA.

COME!
COME, FOR YOU HAVE LOST!

SSSSSSSSS

SSSSSSSSS

tap
tap

ADDIDAS?
HEAR ME?

DRRRiiiiNG
DRRRiiiiiiiNG
HELLO?
IT'S ME!
IT'S YOU?
SAY GOOD-BYE...
YOU'RE LEAVING?
WHERE ARE YOU GOING?
FINISHED...
THIS WORLD FINISHED.
YOU MAKE NEW ...
WAIT, I...
I DON'T KNOW WHAT I'M SUPPOSED...
MAKE PRETTY.
EXACTLY AS YOU LIKE...
GOOD-BYE NOW...
WHERE YOU'RE GOING I CAN NEVER SEE YOU AGAIN?
IT'S THE OPPOSITE.
I DON'T UNDERSTAND.

MAKE THE WORLD THERE WHERE YOU ARE...
SO I'M...
YES.
GOODBYE, ADDIDAS.
LOVE YOU...
MUCH...
ME TOO, ME TOO!
GOODBYE! GOODBYE!
CLICK...

GOODBYE!
WAIT!!

IT'S OVER... YOU'VE LOST... WE ARE WITHIN THE VIRUS...
COMPLETELY MINE... THERE IS NOTHING YOU CAN DO...
NO...
WAIT...

LOOK!

IS THAT WHAT YOU WANT?
TO DESTROY THE WORLD?

HOW DARE YOU?
WHO DO YOU THINK YOU ARE?
THOSE PEOPLE ALL LIVED... THEY HAD WISHES, THEY HAD DREAMS... THEY WERE HAPPY, THEY WERE SAD...
THEY WERE ALIVE...

IT WASN'T A REAL WORLD...

THEY WEREN'T REAL PEOPLE...
WHAT ARE REAL PEOPLE?

LOOK!

NOT REAL PEOPLE?

EVERYTHING CAN RETURN TO HOW IT WAS BEFORE... YOU...YOUR MOTHER...YOUR FATHER... *THE WORLD.*

NO...

I'M AN ACCIDENT.
NOTHING BUT AN ACCIDENT.

I MAKE NEW...

SNIFF...
GOOD-BYE NOW.

YOU...YOU CANNOT MAKE ME DISAPPEAR...
NO...
BUT I WILL TRANSFORM YOU... BECAUSE YOU'RE UGLY THE WAY YOU ARE!

LETTER "E"...

I'M GOING TO TURN YOU INTO AN "EARTHWORM"...

YOU WILL NEVER SEE ANYONE AGAIN...
YOU WILL NEVER SEE YOUR FATHER...

MY FATHER DISCOVERS A NEW WORLD EVERYDAY ...
HE'S IN YOUR HOTEL FOR ALL ETERNITY.

SSSSSSSSSS... IMPOSSIBLE!
WELL, HE IS. I BROUGHT HIM THERE!

OKAY... SO...
"E"...

S SS SSS SSSS

"EARTHWORM"!!

WAI--

WAIT
WAIT
WAIT
WAIT
WAIT
WAIT
WAIT
WAIT
WAIT
WAIT
WAIT
WAIT
WAIT
WAIT
WAIT
WAIT
WAIT
WAIT
WAIT
WAIT

WELL... THERE WE GO...
I JUST NEED TO FIND THOSE TWO KIDS NOW!

THEY'LL FIND THE DOOR EVENTUALLY.

SHE'S NOT COMING BACK.
NO.

BUT NEITHER IS HE.
NO.

JIM!
DAD!

PFFFFFT... THIS IS STARTING TO BORE ME!
I WISH THEY WOULD JUST STOP ACTING LIKE THIS AND GO BACK TO THE WAY THEY WERE!!

HA HA HA HA HA HA!
I CAN'T REMEMBER HOW LONG IT TAKES.

WE HAVE TO OPEN SOME DOORS...
WHAT DO YOU MEAN?
WE HAVE TO OPEN SOME DOORS UNTIL WE FIND THE BASEMENT.

WINSTON!

I'M SICK OF THIS...
I SWEAR.
I'M SICK OF THIS...

AND IF SHE FAILED?
AND IF *HE'S* WAITING FOR US?

WELL, WE CAN'T KNOW...
BUT IN ANY CASE, WE DON'T KNOW JACK ANYWAYS!

I'M GOING...

?!

WHERE ARE WE?!
I'VE NEVER SEEN ANYTHING LIKE IT...

WAIT!

COME ON, SHELL, DON'T BE AFRAID...
ADDIDAS DID THIS!
HE DIDN'T DO THIS!

HOW DO YOU KNOW?

LOOK AROUND!
IT'S BEAUTIFUL!!
SIMPLE AS THAT!

HM...

VOILA...

ADDIDAS!
WHAT IS ALL THIS?

IT'S JUST THE BEGINNING...

AND THAT?
SAY... WHAT IS THAT?

THIS?
THIS IS A BOOK...
OH, YEAH?

FOR CROSSWORDS...
IT'S SUPER HANDY FOR DOING CROSSWORDS...
...AND OTHER THINGS.

COMPLETE
DICTIONARY

IT BELONGED TO MY MOTHER.
I SEE...

UM...
WE KNOW WHERE YOUR MOM IS...
YES, YES,
I KNOW TOO.

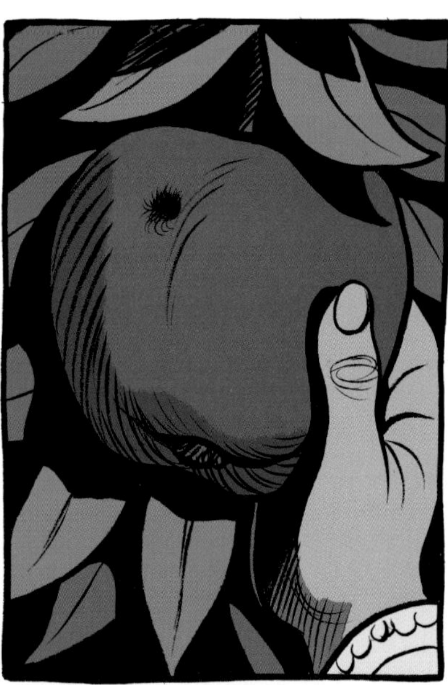

AND HIM? THE... IS HE...?
HE IS NOTHING ANYMORE.

CRRÕÔK
....

MMM... MUNCH...
IT'S GOOD!
WANT SOME?

?!

BLECH!

GULP...
NO THANKS!
BLECH!
I SWALLOWED A PIECE!

A PIECE OF WHAT?
BAH...
NOTHING.
NO, NOTHING.

HM...

OKAY...
ARE YOU GOING TO SHOW US THAT BOOK?

ARE YOU READY?

NOW, WE HAVE TO INVENT EVERYTHING!
WE WILL INVENT EVERYTHING!

BANK

WAZEM – FREDERIK · MAI 2008

END